Golden Harvest

The story of daffodil growing in Cornwall and the Isles of Scilly

Golden Harvest

The story of daffodil growing in
Cornwall and the Isles of Scilly

by Andrew Tompsett

foreword by Bertie Ross
Secretary and Keeper of the Records,
Duchy of Cornwall

Alison Hodge

First published in 2006 by
Alison Hodge, Bosulval, Newmill, Penzance, Cornwall TR20 8XA, UK
www.alison-hodge.co.uk
info@alison-hodge.co.uk

ISBN-13 978-0-906720-46-X
ISBN-10 0-906720-46-X

British Library Cataloguing-in-Publication Data
A catalogue record for this book is available from the British Library.

Cover design by Christopher Laughton, based on a photograph by Peter Phelan

Preparation of images by Peter Phelan, Prophoto Ltd.
www.prophoto-international.com

Edited, designed and originated by
BDP – Book Design and Production,
Penzance, Cornwall
www.bookdevelopment.co.uk

Printed and bound in Singapore

Photo facing title page: Flower power in Cornwall.

Contents

Foreword

Daffodil growing has been an important industry in Cornwall and the Isles of Scilly for over 100 years. The Isles took the initiative when tenant farmers sent their early flowers to London towards the end of the nineteenth century. They were closely followed by growers in West Cornwall and the Tamar Valley.

Over the years the trade grew, bringing prosperity to each area in turn. Despite setbacks from wars, pests and diseases, the vagaries of the weather and, latterly, the increasing impact of flower imports, the industry remains strong by combining the best of traditional knowledge and progressive methods. Cornwall and the Isles of Scilly supply flowers and bulbs to all parts of the UK, to mainland Europe and the USA, bringing pleasure to millions, and employment and profit to the county.

This pictorial account traces the development of the industry, and provides guidance for gardeners and growers in the art and practice of daffodil growing for profit or pleasure.

At a time when the pressures on the growing industry in the South West are as great as they have ever been, I am delighted to welcome the publication of this long-overdue book. It draws attention to the traditions and expertise of those involved – both past and present. Flower growing has been an important contributor, not only to the local economies, but also to the management of the landscape and environment that are valued by the many who live in and visit the area.

Personally, I find the brightness that daffodils bring in the darkening days of November, and the promise of spring in the early months of the new year, a very special pleasure. What they mean to the communities where they are grown, and to the final customers who buy them is recognized and strongly supported by the Duchy of Cornwall.

No other book will appeal so readily to all who, each year, await these harbingers of spring and would, perhaps, like to know more about this most British of flowers, which is so much a part of the Cornish landscape and culture.

W.R.A. ROSS
SECRETARY AND KEEPER OF THE RECORDS,
DUCHY OF CORNWALL

Harbingers of spring, daffodils defy the weather.

Introduction

There are many reasons for wanting to write this book, but primarily it was a fascination with bulbs, especially daffodils, coupled with a desire to tell the story of their cultivation in Cornwall and the Isles of Scilly – a story which spans more than a century.

I hope *Golden Harvest* will provide enough history, science, and horticultural interest, together with a few personal reminiscences, to appeal to a wide readership – especially all those who love daffodils, the county of Cornwall and the Isles of Scilly, or who just experience the thrill of growing plants.

Bulbs are one of the plant world's most advanced survival adaptations. They are virtual time capsules complete with everything necessary for growth, flowering and reproduction in due season. We have learnt, sometimes to our cost, that bulbs retain within them a 'memory' of the recent past, including any ill treatment they may have received at our hands. They are naturally packaged, ready to respond to our bidding – assuming that we understand their basic needs, which are, in fact, rather few.

It was the intention of the late Leslie Major to write a book such as this. He was a daffodil enthusiast, residing near Launceston on the borders of Devon and Cornwall, with a great interest in the West Country crop. I have drawn on some of his notes, and in particular his recollections of events around the middle of the twentieth century and production in the Tamar Valley, an area which he particularly loved.

It is also fitting to acknowledge the role of the Rosewarne Experimental Horticulture Station at Camborne, and those who worked there who sought to support and encourage the industry. During its 38-year existence, Rosewarne's trials explored virtually every aspect of daffodil growing, and the Station raised many new varieties which are the mainstay of the industry today. Rosewarne touched the lives of many horticulturists and scientists who either worked there or were associated with the Station over the years.

Throughout the planning and production of this book, photographer Peter Phelan has been a constant and enthusiastic partner. Without his contribution of pictures, taken in all weathers on daffodil farms in the county, this illustrated account would have been incomplete. I am also grateful to him for his final preparation of the images.

While writing this book I have been reminded of how much there is to say about daffodils, and about those who have grown and studied them, and continue to do so. I hope that some of this evolving story will add to our appreciation of this colourful and interesting crop, which adorns the county each spring.

It is to the Rosewarne staff, and the many friends and supporters of Rosewarne, that this book is dedicated.

Andrew Tompsett, 2006

The author admires a fine batch of split-corona daffodils.

1

The Romance of Daffodils, Origins and Early Days

The romance of daffodils

Cornwall may not be the ancestral home of daffodils, but it is one of the best places in the world to grow them. No single geographical location is so suited to the whole narcissus tribe, and the juxtaposition of Cornwall and the Isles of Scilly makes possible the cultivation of all types, from trumpet daffodils to the heat-loving tazettas.

It may also be argued that no other area in the world has contributed more in terms of new varieties and technical developments, and the sheer love of daffodils. Also, there is little doubt that the famous hatbox sent from the Isles of Scilly to London in about 1870 was the first long-distance 'export' of daffodils, and from this developed a successful industry.

In seeking to describe daffodil growing, and to trace the crop's development in Cornwall, it is worth considering the basis for the British love of daffodils, for it is upon this that the industry relies for its prosperity. To many

people, daffodils evoke feelings that exceed, or at least differ from those that we have for other flowers. Perhaps it is the determination with which they defy the weather, thrusting up from the ground in the depth of winter. Then, before almost any other flower dares to show itself, daffodils are there, untended, undemanding, with gay abandon. From Land's End to John o'Groat's, a succession of daffodils is welcomed as they greet the brighter days.

In Cornwall, daffodils bloom long before spring arrives. While living on the Isles of Scilly, Mary Wilson, wife of the former British Prime Minister, chose some perceptive words to describe the Cornish spring: 'Primroses, daffodils, jasmine and crocus, pale chilly flowers of hesitant spring'.

'Hesitant spring', yes, a fickle, tantalizing thing; here today, invariably gone tomorrow. However, it does have advantages for the grower, since a sequence of varieties can be arranged to give a succession of bloom not

Daffodils reflect the winter sunshine, brightening this visit to the boating lake, Coronation Park, Helston.

Daffodils defy the weather (above), and inspire the flower-arranger (below).

achievable elsewhere. We need not, like poet Robert Herrick, 'weep to see you haste away so soon', as we can be assured of a host of different varieties following on week by week.

For most people, the sight of daffodils creates optimistic feelings as the days gradually lengthen to dispel the gloom of winter. Daffodil breeder and poet, Alec Gray, in his poems *To Scilly*, sees the gales and decay of autumn as a prelude to the new season's shoots. Despite storms, 'great winds that sweep the sea, laying the glory of the garden low', he takes heart from the fact that, 'Here, before winter, autumn can despoil, the daffodils are green above the soil.'

Wordsworth's *Daffodils*, at Ullswater, Britain's favourite poem and said to be embedded in our culture, may suffer from over-use, but were we to hear these words for the first time, they would surely sum up our feelings perfectly:

The simplicity and cheerful permanence of naturalized daffodils seems appropriate here.

Ten thousand saw I at a glance,
Tossing their heads in sprightly dance.

And then my heart with pleasure fills,
And dances with the daffodils.

Shakespeare's description of daffodils, 'That come before the swallow dares', is still true, but at the other end of the year, on the Isles of Scilly, many are coaxed into flower before the last of the swallows have departed.

Origins

The centre of density and greatest diversity of the genus *Narcissus* is concentrated in the Iberian Peninsula, the Southern Alps and the Mediterranean, with few species, other than *N. tazetta*, coming from beyond this. Members of the same natural order, the Amaryllids, are widespread in both the Northern and Southern hemispheres, but no narcissi originate south of the Equator. It is entirely due to human activity that they can now be found on every continent, except Antarctica.

Daffodils find conditions in the cool south of Australia and New Zealand very congenial, and interest in the flower is very strong in the USA, where commercial production is, of necessity, located in the cool, mild Washington State, in the north-west of the country. In South Africa, even at altitude, winters are barely cold enough for daffodils, while in Europe the maritime nations provide the best conditions for their cultivation and long-term survival.

Such a popular and easily transported plant as narcissus has resulted in bulbs being taken around the world by travellers and traders, and it is impossible to define precisely the origins of some of the species. The greatest wanderer

The Wild English Daffodil, or Lent Lily, Narcissus pseudonarcissus, *is occasionally found in cool, damp meadows in the South West of England. It spreads freely by seed.*

has been *Narcissus tazetta*, a bulb requiring a hot summer and mild winter, which is found in a natural or semi-natural state from the Canary Islands in the west, along the Mediterranean coast, via Syria into northern India, China and Japan.

The only species generally accepted as native to Britain is the Wild English Daffodil, or Lent Lily (*Narcissus pseudonarcissus*). This small daffodil is now to be found throughout England and much of Scotland, with the greatest concentration and oldest populations in the South and West, and as far north as the Lake District. There are several different forms of the Lent Lily, an attractive sub-species being the Tenby Daffodil (*N. pseudonarcissus obvallaris*), originally associated with Pembrokeshire, but now widespread. These small daffodils are ideal for naturalizing in grass, and will often spread by seed.

A flower well known throughout Britain is 'Van Sion', a pale, double Lent Lily, also known as 'Telamonius Plenus'. Early in the twentieth century, it was widely grown in nurseries from where, along with many other old varieties, it has been discarded. It persists, semi-wild, provided it is not smothered by coarse vegetation. It too is variable, some strains having double segments confined within the trumpet, and others having a 'burst open' appearance. This is a very ancient flower, first recorded before 1620. It is also known as the 'Guernsey Cabbage Daffodil', a name it really does not deserve.

The Tenby Daffodil, Narcissus pseudonarcissus obvallaris, *is one of the best small daffodils for naturalizing. It is one of the many old, commercial varieties found scattered throughout the Isles of Scilly.*

While the character of *Narcissus pseudonarcissus* shows clearly in our present-day, large-flowered daffodils, most smaller-flowered varieties have been bred from other groups, such as *N. triandrus, N. cyclamineus, N. jonquilla, N. tazetta,* and *N. poeticus.* Hybrids from these retain many characteristics of the parents, and so generally can be neatly classified into one of the 11 divisions of daffodils defined by the Royal Horticultural Society (RHS). As usual, there are exceptions, so another division has been created for the misfits, with 'Tête à Tête' probably the best-known example – a marriage of *N. tazetta* and *N. cyclamineus.* The classification of daffodils is elaborated upon in Chapter 3, 'Daffodils, narcissi and the RHS'. Since about 1800, so many species have contributed to the range of colour and form in modern daffodils that the science of genetics is scarcely able to unravel the situation.

Most commercial cut-flower daffodils are trumpets, large-cupped types or large doubles.

The small-cupped varieties and 'Pheasant's eye' kinds, once popular cut flowers, declined with the coming of bud marketing, their thin stems and slim buds looking less impressive. While single-headed daffodils are derived mainly from sub-species of *Narcissus pseudonarcissus,* admixture with *N. poeticus* genes gives the bold colours we associate with the later flowering, small-cupped ones.

The origin of *Narcissus triandrus* is based firmly in Spain and Portugal. The species is not robust; indeed, it can be short lived in cultivation, and reproduces best from seed. Normally multi-headed, hybrids between *N. triandrus* and other types are usually more robust

Narcissus cyclamineus is a real gem among the small, wild species. First recorded in the seventeenth century, it was thought to be extinct, but was rediscovered in Portugal in 1885. It has never been common or easy to grow. However, in the hands of the plant breeder

In Narcissus cyclamineus, *breeders struck a rich vein from which to refine superb garden varieties.*

it has begotten some of our finest dwarf and medium-sized garden varieties. The species has one flower per stem, and fully reflexed petals in the form of a cyclamen flower. The graceful backward sweep of the petals of cyclamineus hybrids makes them instantly recognizable. When crossed with tazettas, flowers are usually multi-headed if the bulbs are large enough.

Narcissus jonquilla, and its related species, originate in southern Spain, and have spread widely. Like *N. triandrus*, *N. jonquilla* is multi-headed, but taller, with narrow, dark green, rush-like leaves and round stems. The outstanding features of jonquils are their clear colour and powerful scent.

Tazetta species have a wide distribution in the hot countries of the Mediterranean and beyond. All are multi-headed and strongly scented, and their hybrids succeed best in the South and West of England. Tazettas in the Northern hemisphere appreciate that most desirable of horticultural micro-climates, the south-facing border backed by a wall, not only for winter protection, but also to ensure as warm a summer as possible. Even then, some varieties, like 'Paper White' and *Narcissus canaliculatus* are reluctant bloomers in the UK. The special heating and smoke treatments used by tazetta growers are described in Chapter 6, 'A burning question'.

Narcissus poeticus (Poet's Narcissus) and related species are the late-flowering, white-petalled 'Pheasant's eye' flowers seen traditionally in cottage gardens. Their flattened flowers have rounded petals and an intense, red-rimmed 'eye'. *N. poeticus* ssp. *recurvus*

Narcissus poeticus *is a European Alpine species.*

possesses a delightful backward sweep and curl to the petals, and is an unforgettable sight when seen *en masse* in Continental Alpine meadows as late as June. The brilliant cup colour of many small-cupped daffodils, contrasting with pure white petals, derives from the thin red rim of the Poet's. It follows that some of the brightest coloured daffodils tend to flower late.

Narcissus bulbocodium, the 'Hoop Petticoat' daffodil, is a true miniature more suited to the Alpine house than the open ground, although the sandy soil of Wisley's 'Alpine meadow' clearly suits it. It is instantly recognizable by its diminutive petals, inflated cups and grassy leaves.

An industry is born

The West Country daffodil industry was born offshore, in the remote, mild but windswept Isles of Scilly, 29 miles west of Land's End. Poverty and hopelessness were the lot of Scillonians until, in 1834, a handsome young man came, cast a critical eye over the Isles and decided to stay.

Augustus Smith was the eldest son of a wealthy Hertfordshire family who, having busied himself with parish affairs in his hometowns of Berkhamsted and Northchurch, sought a wider stage on which to practise his undoubted administrative ability. According to Mike Nelhams (at the time of writing, Curator of Tresco Abbey Garden), when the opportu-

Scillonian farmer William Trevellick in his daffodil fields at Rocky Hill, St Mary's, c. 1900.

nity came to become Lord Proprietor of the Isles, he took up the challenge with energy and awesome determination.

When Augustus Smith arrived on the Scillies to stamp his authority on the impoverished Islanders, not everyone approved of his autocratic manner. Initially, he won few hearts, and many Scillonians resented his intrusion into their way of life. A dynamic personality, he reformed the rules affecting farm succession, built schools, and enforced education by fining parents if their child did not attend. He completed the building of churches, extended St Mary's quay, and gave a new lease of life to the Islands' shipbuilding industry. His enterprises included the removal of the impoverished inhabitants of the island of Samson to create a deer park; raising ostriches for their fashionable feathers, and planting his dream garden around the ruins of the old Tresco Abbey, which, despite the unpromising prospect, has become one of the world's great gardens.

William Trevellick and his wife, family and pickers in the glasshouse at Rocky Hill, where flowers were brought into bloom before being sent to market, c. 1900.

Augustus Smith's arrival heralded a time of change on the Islands: potato growers were unable to raise the standard of their crops to compete with those on the Channel Islands, and iron-built, steam-powered ships were replacing the traditional wooden-hulled ships made on St Mary's. However, there soon came better news: the completion of the Great Western Railway link from Penzance to London in 1859 meant that the capital might provide a realistic new market for the Islands' produce.

Early one late-January morning, about 1870, Scillonian farmer William Trevellick may have donned his heavy oilskin coat and boots and, opening the back door of the farmhouse, stepped outside. He became aware of daffodils and narcissi all along the tracks and stone-built hedges of Rocky Hill Farm, gleaming in the half-light. They had already been flowering for some while, as they did each January, for as long as he could remember. But he had never seen them look as bright as they did on this particular morning. He recalled someone saying that 'up country', narcissi flowered around St David's day – more than a month away. The thought obsessed him for several days.

Might there be a market for early daffodils on the mainland? Trevellick gathered some 30

The 'Golden Mile', east of Penzance, is a prime site for early horticulture (overleaf).

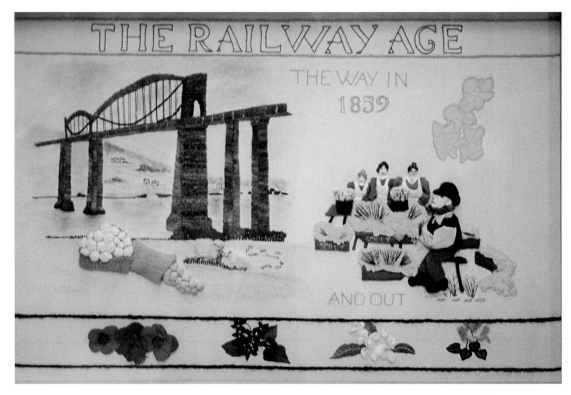

The Trevellas needlework picture in Redruth shows the importance of the railway to Cornwall's produce.

bunches of 'Scilly White', 'Soleil d'Or', 'Gloriosus' and Old English daffodils; packed them upright in an old hatbox; fastened the lid, and attached to it a label on which he inscribed: 'Scilly, Penzance, Covent Garden, London'. Then he took it to the weekly freighter anchored at St Mary's quay. Fourteen days later, he received a letter from a general produce salesman in Covent Garden, to which was attached payment of seven shillings and sixpence (37½ pence)! Encouraged, he sent another box, for which he soon received £1. Clearly, there was a demand for spring flowers in the capital. From then on, William and several neighbours began to assemble the many semi-wild daffodils that were to be found in the hedgerows and byways of Rocky Hill, Holy Vale and Watergate.

Co-operating with his neighbours, Richard Mumford, Hugh Watts and Mr W.M. Gluyas,

Trevellick cultivated daffodils for the next two years. Their efforts were noticed by Thomas Algernon Dorrien-Smith, nephew of Augustus Smith, and some accounts state that it was actually he who initiated the whole idea of marketing the flowers. Whatever the truth, Dorrien-Smith was a man quick to realize the potential for the Scillies' daffodil crop, whereupon he prudently invested money in its development.

Converting the idea into an economic reality, Dorrien-Smith visited Holland, Belgium and the Channel Islands in 1882, where he bought about 190 different varieties of daffodils. New bulbs were also obtained from Ware of Tooting, and Barr & Sons of Covent Garden. In all he spent £10,000 on bulb stocks, which he supplied to his tenants, together with what were referred to as 'bulb houses' used for bulb forcing and tomato growing. He was also active in encouraging the planting of shelter hedges to protect the crops – a process that began to establish the layout and character of the Islands as we still see them today.

The first recorded cargo of flower exports was a shipment of 65 tons (59 tonnes) in 1885. This increased steadily to 700 tons (635 tonnes) in 1905. However, it is worth recording that the sturdy, locally made wooden boxes in which the flowers travelled, probably weighed almost as much as the flowers themselves.

Early accounts state that among a range of narcissi growing on the Isles of Scilly in the nineteenth century, 'Scilly White' and 'Soleil d'Or' were particularly numerous. These are of Mediterranean origin, but they appear to have flourished on the Islands unaided for generations. At that time 'Scilly Whites' also grew on St Michael's Mount in Mount's Bay, and on Mont-Saint-Michel on the Normandy coast in France. Tresco Abbey was linked with Benedictine monasteries at the two 'Mounts', and at Tavistock, so it seems likely that this is the route by which they came to West Cornwall. One suggestion is that the rounded, shiny, 'conker-brown' tazetta bulb was a desirable object in itself, and a suitable gift for a friend or brother of the Order. Other, less worthy possibilities have been suggested, perhaps relating to services rendered to smugglers, known as 'fair traders'.

In 1885, Andrew Lawry began daffodil farming at Varfell, Penzance, overlooking St Michael's Mount at the eastern end of the south-facing hillside known as the 'Golden Mile'. He probably became aware of Scillonian flowers being transferred from steamship to rail in Penzance, and it is thought that he was the first commercial daffodil grower on the Cornish mainland. At the beginning of the twenty-first century, Varfell is still a prime site for early horticulture. This particular stretch of land has been cropped with early potatoes, broccoli (winter cauliflower) and bulbs for generations. In its alkaline soils, whether due to aeons of wind-blown dune-sand or applications of this calcareous material in more recent times, the brassica family have been grown without fear of clubroot disease. Today, Varfell Farm is the world's largest daffodil producer, with over 400 hectares (1,000 acres) of bulbs, and an annual replant of over 2,500 tonnes.

> There is good reason to believe that owing to its mild and salubrious climate the inhabitants of West Cornwall … will in years to come be drawn more and more strongly towards an industry which … seems entirely suited to the genius of the Cornish people. That it can become a source of considerable profit, wherever intelligence and industry are found combined, is beyond question.

So wrote William Page, in the section on horticulture in the *Victoria History of Cornwall*, published in 1906. Clearly, there was great enthusiasm for the potential of early horticulture to generate income and gainful employment for a large number of people.

Since the early twentieth century, West Cornwall has produced the earliest open-ground flowers and vegetables in the UK. The diversity of cropping is now much reduced, as imports from the Mediterranean and further afield have eroded the area's advantage. However, the daffodil crop has withstood the tide of competition, and Cornwall still produces the country's earliest outdoor flowers – a fact which, by a piece of good luck, the world's hotter climes cannot challenge, due to the daffodil's preference for our cool, temperate climate.

2

The Daffodil Industry Today

How the crop is grown

The daffodil crop is unusual in that there are two products – flowers and bulbs. The relative value of these two commodities fluctuates over the years and affects how the crop is grown. Cornwall's greatest advantage is in producing flowers early and over a long season, but the county also has some advantages in bulb production. East of England counties, with their later, more concentrated flowering season and broad acres of flat land, have traditionally focused on the bulb trade, with considerable quantities 'forced' under heated glass.

It is generally agreed that the optimum life of a daffodil crop is two or three years. However, if the bulb trade undergoes a period of oversupply and depressed prices, the emphasis, especially in Cornwall, moves more towards flowers, with most bulbs remaining in the ground for three and sometimes four years. By the end of such an extended period,

the plants will have become overcrowded and the bulb weight may not have increased much beyond that of a two-year crop. The bulbs will be smaller and possibly of reduced quality, and will carry a greater risk of disease. This is important because the bulbs that the grower harvests provide not only those for sale, but also planting stock for the future.

The Isles of Scilly differ from the mainland. Flower income is a higher priority there, and crops regularly remain in the ground for four or more years. Fortunately, this suits 'Soleil d'Or' and the other tazettas that are grown there.

The powerhouse of any plant is its area of healthy leaf, since this determines the amount of solar energy that it can absorb. Daffodils grow during the dull days of winter and spring when days are short and sunshine weak. In early summer, rising temperatures begin to stress the plants, which then start to die off. The grower, wishing to lift for an early bulb market, may

Picking daffodils at Halvose Farm, Manaccan, 2003. In the daffodil season, warm, sunny days are few. Note the 'pencil' stage picking, gloves to protect against 'lily rash', and a flower pot to hold rubber bands.

On Cornish farms, bulb planters are busy throughout July and August, before the land becomes too wet (above). The planter hopper can hold up to a tonne of bulbs (below).

welcome this and may even destroy the leaf to facilitate early lifting. However, to achieve the greatest bulb increase, the grower needs to protect the foliage from damage and disease, so enabling the plants to take full advantage of the improving weather and lengthening days in April and May. How this is done is described later in 'Preserving the leaf'.

The growing cycle begins with planting, using a machine with a tractor driver and one person controlling the flow of bulbs down the chutes and into the twin furrows that close up as it passes. Another tractor with bin tipper stands ready to refill the planter hopper on the field margin (headland). The land will have been well cultivated in advance, the pH (acidity or alkalinity) checked to ensure that it is not below pH 6.0, and a high potash compound fertilizer incorporated.

Planting daffodil bulbs on St Martin's, Isles of Scilly. A plough covers a row of hand-planted bulbs, c. 1910 (above). Bulbs were placed by hand in an open plough furrow until the mid-twentieth century (below).

Until about 1950, planting was highly labour-intensive. As a horse- or tractor-drawn plough turned each furrow, the bulbs were hand-placed in a line and covered by the next furrow slice. After five or six rows, three furrows were turned over, leaving a path for the pickers and any handwork. A few years later, to recover the bulbs, the ploughman's skill, and that of the original planters, would be put to the test. The plough now had to be set to travel just below the bulbs, and close enough for them to be picked off the upturned furrow row by row. Some early experiments showed that a 'bed' system produces a high yield because the plants are evenly spaced. However, in practice, many bulbs were damaged or left behind by the plough. In Holland, beds are still used, and machines have been developed to plant and harvest such bulbs on their (mostly)

sandy soils. In Cornwall, the bed system persisted for many years, and ancient beds of daffodils can still be seen on abandoned plots in West Penwith and on the Isles of Scilly.

The change to growing bulbs in ridges followed the development of machines for planting and lifting potatoes. Before the modern bulb planter appeared, planting was still done by hand with the bulbs scattered into 'U'-shaped furrows. The soil was then split back over them with ridging 'bodies' mounted on the front of the tractor. With bulbs in ridges, growers could use an 'elevator-digger', which undercuts the bulbs, raising them up over a riddle and leaving them to dry on the surface in 'windrows'.

Of course, planting machines scatter the bulbs in the furrows and do not place them upright as in the old days, or as one might do in the garden. A little of the uniformity of growth that accompanies hand placement has been lost, but this is a minor detail in today's highly mechanized and cost-conscious industry.

Planting normally takes place travelling up and down a field, since working across a slope can cause the machine to 'crab' sideways with disastrous consequences. However, this direction of planting increases the risk of soil erosion, with silt in watercourses and mud on roads. To minimize run-off, growers try to retain some weed cover over the soil in winter. An extension of this idea is to sow barley over the bulb field in autumn. The cereal stabilizes the soil, and can be destroyed later before it becomes a problem. An alternative is to maintain a strip of grass as a silt trap at the bottom of the field. A recent development, borrowed from potato growing, is to de-stone the soil before planting to facilitate lifting the crop and reduce bulb bruising. The larger stones are not

removed from the field, but buried in furrows where they assist drainage.

Bulbs are planted early in Cornwall, mostly before the end of August. This produces early flowers and good bulb growth. Early planting is not considered so important in Eastern England, and is avoided in Holland because warm soil can encourage disease. Another factor favouring early planting in Cornwall is the deteriorating weather and heavier soil conditions after the end of August.

Weed control on both newly planted areas and older crops is a vital autumn operation. Since the mid 1960s, various herbicides have been used, and bulb crops have benefited enormously from reduced weed competition and cleaner conditions for harvesting. However, there can be problems with complete weed control, especially on warm, south-facing slopes. Trials have shown that bare soil is warmer than weed-covered ground, and this can encourage basal rot disease. So the aim is usually to reduce weeds rather than totally eliminate them. Provided that weeds do not compete aggressively during the growing season, or clog up the bulb harvester, they are helpful in reducing soil erosion, while also providing cleaner conditions underfoot for the pickers. Finches, particularly linnets, like to gather on these winter supplies of weed seeds.

The early stages of growth are the best times to inspect the crop for 'rogues' and viruses, or the presence of a pest such as eelworm. Rogues are those bulbs of another variety, which have become mixed into the stock accidentally. The roguing iron – a tool uniquely known to bulb growers – can, in skilled hands, winkle out a rogue or virus-infected plant without disturbing neighbouring plants.

As the crops come into bud, picking and marketing are the top priority. Methods differ

Left: The roguing iron – a tool uniquely known to bulb growers – is used to winkle out a 'rogue' bulb. Right: A comparison of the slightly open tazetta narcissus flowers (var. 'Royal Connection'), which are pulled, and the tight buds of daffodils, which are snapped, shows the extra length of the former.

between the Scillies and the mainland. In Cornwall, large gangs of pickers are required, and questions of their availability and the social consequences are arising. Formerly, local labour met the need, but increasingly the larger growers employ gangs of foreign workers (see below, 'A modern industry'). For those prepared to do this work, the piecework rates offered are quite attractive. However, it has to be admitted that in the daffodil season warm, sunny days are rather few. More likely there will be wind and rain, with mud underfoot and backache at the end of the day!

On the Islands there is a different tradition, as many farms are family units. Men brave the elements while the women bunch, 'tie' and pack the flowers indoors. Rubber bands replaced raffia ties in the 1930s, and bunches are no longer 'faced' as they used to be. Unlike daffodils that are easily snapped off, the varieties grown on the Islands have tough stems and are pulled – a practice that does not harm the bulb. This gives extra length, but pulling flowers from newly planted bulbs must be done with care, otherwise the bulbs themselves can be dislodged. The multi-headed narcissi popular on the Scillies are gathered in a slightly more open state than the standard daffodil.

The move towards picking and marketing daffodils in bud, which began during the 1960s, has led to the universal use of cold stores to arrest development. This is critical, as consignments of daffodils can be rejected by the market if the buds are opening. All farms prevent this by holding the bunches at 1–2° C, in complete contrast to practices in the distant

A gas burner is sometimes used to scorch off the foliage and facilitate bulb lifting (above).
Below: Bulb harvesting in two stages. First, bulbs are lifted into 'windrows', where they dry for a few days,
and then they can be picked up by hand or machine – increasingly the latter.

Picking up bulbs on stony ground is not the most popular job.

past, when flowers were placed in greenhouses to open them before despatch. The modern methods of picking and handling, dense packing, and refrigerated transport, all aim at ensuring that the buds do not open and spoil during transit to markets at home or overseas.

After flower picking, the grower needs to keep watch for leaf diseases. Modern fungicides are very efficient, requiring just a few ounces per acre, but they only protect against incoming fungal spores. Once disease has taken hold, it can develop rapidly, causing premature leaf death (senescence), with smaller bulbs and fewer flowers the next year.

Operations in the summer depend upon whether the bulbs stay in the ground, or are lifted for sale and replanting. If they are to remain, the longer the leaf stays green the better. However, if lifting is required, it is easier if the leaf is either dead, removed mechanically, or burnt. Gas burning machines are sometimes used,

replacing the former sulphuric acid spray applied by contractor. Any other herbicide at this stage incurs a risk of severe damage to the bulbs.

June is a critical time for bulb lifting, and growers hope for a dry month. Time is limited since, by August, some varieties may begin to re-root and would be damaged if taken up. Fortunately, June is the driest month of the year in Cornwall, although it still has an average of 13 days with rain. Bulbs can be left to dry on the soil surface for several days, so-called 'windrow drying', or taken indoors where they need artificial drying with hot air. Windrow drying avoids the use of energy, but leaves the grower at the mercy of the weather; either wet or sunburnt bulbs are possible. Increasingly, bulbs are picked up by machine but, where the land is stony, handwork is still used. Lincolnshire growers led the way in 'complete' harvesting into trailers or bulk bins, followed immediately by drying with ducted hot air.

After a suitable period of drying and ripening, the next operations are riddling, brushing, sorting and grading. At this stage, bulbs which are to be sold are separated from those needed for replanting. Unlike many crops, where the grower will purchase new 'seed' each year, the bulb grower generally prefers to retain his own stock rather than risk buying in bulbs of unknown performance from elsewhere. In considering which bulbs to replant, he has a further choice: if the larger bulbs are sold consistently, over the years there will be a weakening of the stock, since these will be the healthiest, with the smaller grades most likely to be carrying virus diseases. The main demand in recent years has been for medium-sized bulbs for pre-packing, so the grower usually retains the 'offsets' and some of the larger bulbs for replanting.

Before planting, bulbs are hot-water treated to ensure freedom from pests. Even where a crop appears perfectly healthy, it never pays to skip this insurance treatment and risk a pest attack. The story of its development is described in Chapter 5, 'A nice warm bath'.

Daffodils are usually planted at 15–18 tonnes per hectare (6–7 tonnes per acre), and 15 cm (6 in.) deep. After two growing seasons the bulb weight should, at least, double; so, to maintain the same acreage, about half of the crop is replanted. Sometimes, a valuable new variety is planted more thinly, to produce more than a doubling in weight, thus enabling a greater acreage to be planted next time.

Cornwall's weather

The climate of South West England owes its remarkable warmth to the Gulf Stream and the mild North Atlantic Drift that sweeps our western shores. Were it not for this maritime influence, Cornwall, lying close to latitude 50° North might have a very different climate – more like Winnipeg and Kiev, which also lie on this line.

The mild winters and cool summers are a direct result of the smoothing effect of the ocean, which causes a merging of the seasons. Rainfall is frequent, occurring in every month, and rapid changes in the weather are a constant topic of conversation.

For the statistically minded, the average 24-hour temperature for West Cornwall varies by only 10° C between winter and summer, from 5.5° C in February to 15.5° C in August. The Isles of Scilly have a similar range, from about 7° C to 16.5° C. Some recent winters have been the warmest on record, with periods in Cornwall averaging over 10° C, causing unwelcome peaks of flowering.

Rainfall in Camborne averages 1,067 mm. (42 in.) a year – a figure that increases considerably on Cornwall's higher moors. On the Isles of Scilly, due to their low profile, rainfall is less, averaging 838 mm. (33 in.) – not dissimilar to that of the Home Counties. The wettest months are October to January, and the driest is June, which is important for bulb harvesting. Gales are frequent, averaging about 16 per annum, and constant air movement off the sea minimizes the effects of frost – one recent

Bulbs are elevated on to an inspection belt, and go from there to a size grader (top left). Extractor fans and ducts remove dust from the grading line (top right). Each size grade is collected into a separate bin (bottom left): medium-sized bulbs are in greatest demand for pre-packs. Rosewarne helped the industry to develop the bin system. The one container serves for drying, warming, dipping and cooling, but can only be moved mechanically (bottom right).

On the mainland, some of the more valuable varieties are protected by a poly-house.

exception being January 1987, when strong easterlies affected the county, killing or severely damaging tender plants. Tresco Abbey Garden suffered huge losses in those frosts, and also in the gales of 1990.

The combination of cool summers, wind, high rainfall and humidity imposes limitations on growing many horticultural crops. This is particularly the case with fruits, which frequently fail to set a full crop, suffering wind scorch and fungal diseases. In times past, well-sheltered walled gardens were highly productive, but the field-scale grower has no such defence against the elements, and has to think very carefully before venturing outside the traditional range of crops such as brassicas, potatoes and daffodils.

Fred Shepherd, the first director of the Rosewarne Experimental Horticulture Station (EHS), from 1951 to 1961 – like Augustus Smith a century before – sought to popular-ize the planting of shelter belts for horticulture. Monterey Pine (*Pinus radiata*) was the favourite, to which he added Monterey Cypress (*Cupressus macrocarpa*) and Leyland Cypress (X *Cupressocyparis leylandii*) with *Escallonia* 'Crimson Spire' as a hedge or ground-level filler. These transformed the Rosewarne microclimate. Fred Shepherd would dryly relate how some onlookers would mutter, 'If this catches on it will ruin the Cornish landscape!'

First in the market

Snowdrops, daffodils, stocks, wallflowers, polyanthus, anemones, irises and violets all convey the welcome news that spring has reached the Isles of Scilly and West Cornwall. That first hatbox packed with narcissi, sent to London by William Trevellick towards the end of the nineteenth century, fetched a remarkably good return for flowers which, as far as we know, were virtually growing wild.

The insatiable demand for spring flowers in the capital in those early days presented an undreamed-of opportunity for West Country growers. Early-flowering varieties were eagerly sought, and still are because of the higher prices paid for early flowers and for bulbs of early varieties. Rosewarne's breeding programme, which ran from 1964 to 1989, had the prime objective of raising earlier field-grown daffodils, while the station also studied cultural techniques that would deliver earlier crops.

The Isles of Scilly have always had the advantage over West Cornwall in producing the earliest flowers of each variety, while West Cornwall is ahead of the growers occupying the steep slopes of the Tamar Valley in the east of the county. Growers in East Anglia lag behind by up to a month at the beginning of the season, although they do catch up and there may be only a few days difference in the flowering of late varieties between west and east. This can be explained by the greater cold requirement of late-flowering varieties; unlike the early ones, they do not benefit from Cornwall's mild weather until they have experienced sufficient chilling.

At the start of the twenty-first century, earliness is still important, but continuity of production is equally so. The greatest problem facing UK growers is the vast year-round array of other flowers in the market and shops, compared with only 20 years ago. Britain attracts flower imports from around the world, often from countries with enviable climates and low labour costs. Today the seasons are blurred, and it seems that spring has lost much of its magic feeling with roses, carnations, freesias, gerberas and chrysanthemums available every day of the year. The daffodil grower's response to this competition and static flower returns has been to expand, cut costs, improve quality and try to provide uniformity and continuity of supply. Three or four months' continuity is required, especially by supermarket buyers.

Expansion of daffodil farms has been made possible by mechanization, herbicides, bud picking, cold storage, and cool-chain distribution in refrigerated trucks, bringing export opportunities. Fortunately, ample healthy land is available in Cornwall, and the county's growers have become well equipped and technically advanced.

On the Isles of Scilly, where farms are much smaller and the availability of sheltered land and labour are strictly limited, growers have had to adopt a different strategy. Each field, or 'square', needs protecting against strong, salt-laden winds that sweep in from the surrounding sea. In the early days, the Scillies grew many of the same varieties as the mainland. However, as Cornwall's daffodil production has expanded, the Scillies have specialized in the scented tazetta type of narcissi. Fortunately, these suit the Isles, and have been a lifeline for the growers. Although they start to flower in September, three months earlier than the mainland's daffodils, growers on the Isles of Scilly also try to supply over a six-month season. This is achieved by growing a range of varieties (listed in Appendix 2), and by applying some very unusual techniques, which are described in Chapter 6, 'A burning question'.

Reaping the wind

Shakespeare's image of dancing daffodils in *The Winter's Tale*, 'That come before the swallow dares, and take the winds of March with beauty' is less poetic for the grower, since the winds that make the flowers dance can become a gale resulting in serious financial loss. This is an ever-present worry, and growers study the weather forecasts, and pick the crop in tight bud if there are reports of an incoming westerly. Storms, especially of hail, can result in losses far exceeding those caused by frost.

The mildest winter temperatures occur near the sea, and in the first half of the twentieth century, to gain a few days advantage, crops were grown on coastal pockets of land or 'quillets'. Derek Tangye, who with his wife left the City to take up flower growing on the cliffs near Lamorna in West Cornwall, describes in his book *Gull on the Roof*, the sense of panic and helplessness as storms swept in across Mount's Bay:

Down we staggered to the lower part of the field and the beam of the torch shone on a sight which resembled a herd of terrified miniature animals tethered to the ground. Nothing we could do would save our harvest.

'Princeps' lingers in cliff pockets, long since abandoned to bracken, brambles and gorse.

On the Isles of Scilly, evergreen hedges are essential to subdue the wind. Duchy of Cornwall tenants plant and maintain neat surrounding 'fences', mainly of *Pittosporum crassifolium* and *Olearia traversii*, two New Zealand evergreens with amazing tolerance to salt-laden winds. A prolonged freeze of -5° C, such as occurred in January 1987, will kill *Pittosporum*, but with its upright habit it is still the preferred species. A mature 3 m. (10 ft.) high hedge, maintained to provide 50 per cent permeability, shelters a strip 18–30 m. (60–100 ft.) wide, and is much more effective than any form of solid barrier.

As daffodil growing in Cornwall expanded into larger units, the small coastal fields and the cliff pockets have reverted to bracken, gorse and brambles. There is now a greater emphasis on renting fresh, more easily worked land. If some natural shelter is available, so much the better, but on the mainland of Cornwall, no

special steps are taken to provide it in today's 'nomadic' culture. Planting ten or so rows of bulbs around the field margin does make the most of any existing shelter, while facilitating turning the spraying machine. Adjacent woodland is also a bonus, the cool shade it provides in the autumn advancing most daffodil varieties.

The grower renting land seeks it in large parcels, to reduce the amount of time spent travelling, transporting the pickers and hauling flowers and bulbs. Parking in narrow lanes presents problems, so pickers are often taken to and from the fields in mini-buses. Winter is the wettest time of the year, and growers have to be careful not to leave mud on the roads.

Preserving the leaf

If daffodils become overcrowded, over-shaded, are cut off too early, or are attacked by leaf disease, the foliage cannot function properly, and the bulbs may fail to flower the next year. The gardener or park keeper may lament the absence of bloom, but commercial growers must act to keep the leaf healthy as long as possible.

Daffodils are superbly designed plants. Their strap-like leaves withstand the wind; the stems, if blown over, straighten up again and, uniquely useful to the flower grower, the naked stems can be picked without removing any of the nourishing leaves. This is not the case with other bulbs such as tulips, lilies and irises, where leaves are sacrificed when cutting the flower. Unlike daffodils, none of these can be grown as dual-purpose crops, their bulbs usually being discarded after harvesting the flowers. Additionally, after flowering, tulip and iris bulbs split up into several daughter bulbs, which may fail to flower the next year. Daffodils (and lilies) do not do this, and so maintain a flowering-sized bulb over many years.

All gardening books advise against tidying up daffodil leaves too early. Most daffodils benefit from their leaves being left until they begin to turn yellow. However, commercial monocultures tend to increase the risk of the foliage dying prematurely due to fungal diseases. These fungal foes are a worrying quartet, as their names suggest: 'Stag', 'White Mould', 'Smoulder' and 'Fire'.

Stag – an abbreviation of the Latin name *Stagonospora*, also known as 'leaf scorch' – is bulb-borne, and persists from year to year in the 'nose' of the bulb, showing in spring as brown leaf tips. White Mould lingers overwinter in leaf debris, shooting out spores as the new growth appears. This disease is particularly troublesome in Cornwall. Smoulder – one of the *Botrytis* family – persists as fungal bodies (sclerotia), often just under the outer skins of the bulbs, whence it infects the new shoot, and later the leaves. It tends to be worst in the east and north of the country. Another

'Fire' (above), which spreads from dead flowers, and 'White Mould' (below), which starts on the tip of the leaf, can quickly destroy the leaves, reducing the next season's flower crop.

A better understanding of leaf diseases, and commercial spraying, has greatly increased yields of both flowers and bulbs.

species of *Botrytis*, the aptly named 'Fire', can destroy the leaf in just a few weeks. Its spores usually infect the flowers as they die, and from here the fungus spreads to the leaves. Although gardeners nip off flowers as they fade to save the plant from producing seeds and reduce the risk of 'Fire', commercial growers find it more economical to protect the leaves with sprays.

Early death of the leaves adversely affects the whole physiology of the plant, since without a sufficient period in which to photosynthesize, it produces a small bulb and may fail to initiate a bud for the next year. Growers judge flowering potential according to bulb size, which for most large-flowered daffodils should be at least 10 cm, and preferably 12 cm, in *circumference*. The word circumference is worth stressing. Believing it to refer to bulb diameter can lead to disappointment.

The use of fungicides began in France in 1885, when copper sulphate and lime were applied to vines, initially to deter pilfering. Amazingly, it prevented mildew, and from this simple observation developed the whole science of crop protection. For many years fungicide spraying has been considered essential for efficient bulb production.

'Bordeaux mixture' – the copper sulphate/ lime mix – was the first fungicide applied to bulbs in the middle of the twentieth century. Tank-mix zineb was an improvement, but was replaced by Benlate, a major step forward in a variety of crops. Today, programmes using carbendazim, Dithane, chlorothalonil, Rovral or strobilurin are used, according to the dictates of the fungi and the weather. Since the materials only protect against incoming disease spores, they must be used before any leaf spotting has occurred. Growers need to apply these fungicides with reference to the picking date, to minimize spray deposit on the product.

At the start of the twenty-first century, West Cornwall and the Isles of Scilly produce about 20 per cent of the world's daffodils.

A modern industry

The UK daffodil industry leads the world in size and technical expertise. Although the Dutch bulb industry is huge, producing all kinds from *Acidanthera* to *Zantedeschia*, Britain grows twice as many daffodils as Holland. Our crop, which remains fairly constant at about 4,000 hectares (10,000 acres), represents about half the world's production. Cornwall's share has risen steadily since the 1970s, from 20 to 40 per cent of the UK crop. The relatively small area of West Cornwall and the Isles of Scilly probably grows almost 20 per cent of the world's daffodils.

Although Cornish growers try to sell as many flowers as possible, one has only to travel through the west of the county in March and April to see numerous fields still yellow with daffodils. This may seem a huge waste, but it is an inevitable consequence of trying to maintain a steady supply of flowers to the markets throughout the winter and spring months.

Many of the golden fields may actually have been picked over once or twice, while still leaving enough to produce a carpet of bloom.

To achieve the essential continuity requires a well-planned sequence of varieties, sufficient pickers, and suitably cool but mild weather. Problems arise if any one of these is lacking – especially the weather, about which one can do nothing. A cold snap can delay development, while a warm, wet period can result in a surge of flowers overwhelming the pickers and the markets. The best strategy is to produce more than is strictly required – hence the golden fields. In a mild spell, the grower tends to concentrate on picking the variety and quality most likely to achieve the best prices. This usually means ignoring first-year flowers, which are smaller and lighter in weight than those from established bulbs.

Another feature of the daffodil scene is the apparent disappearance of the crop between

Left: A partially picked crop: this amount of wastage is quite common. The bulbs have been grown in ridges – a practice that followed the development of machines for potato growing. Above left: A 'checker' keeps a tally of every picker's bunches, which determines their pay. Above right: A modern packing shed.

one year and the next. Last year's splash of gold in the landscape may have completely disappeared. A closer look, however, may reveal some 'ground keepers' that evaded the harvester, appearing lost and doomed among a following crop of cabbages.

Some of Cornwall's larger bulb farms have specialized to the point where they no longer grow any other crop. The daffodil grower's year has two busy periods: the flower season and the bulb harvest, which each occupy three or four months. These labour peaks can clash with the demands of other crops, which are usually less profitable than bulb growing. Bulbs require a long 'break' before they can be planted again

on the same field. The problem is overcome by renting land from other farmers for a three-year period. 'Virgin land', which has never grown daffodils before, is a definite advantage.

In addition to having a good climate for daffodils, Cornwall also has excellent soils, easily worked and naturally well drained. However, small fields, slopes and stones all increase costs compared with the flat lands of East Anglia. Cornwall has a trump card when it comes to exporting bulbs since many fields are free from Potato Cyst Nematode (PCN). Potato eelworm does not attack bulbs, but soil adhering to bulbs can carry the pest. All countries demand a soil-free consignment, but North

Cornish daffodils are distributed daily by road to the markets.

America and Scandinavia go further, requiring a soil test to ensure freedom from this pest.

One of the most pressing concerns has been the availability of labour to pick the flowers. While mechanical harvesting, or mechanical aids, are used for many crops, there is little prospect of replacing hand labour for gathering flowers. When harvesting outdoor daffodils, pickers need to pass through the crop several times, and are expected to leave the foliage undamaged to feed the bulb. Bulbs grown in boxes under glass usually grow more uniformly, and are generally destroyed after cropping. A system exists where the crop travels by conveyor from the glasshouse to the pack-house, where both stems and leaves are cut. Flowers with leaves (with 'spike') attract a higher price.

In season, Cornwall requires several thousand pickers every day. Although some winter days can be comparatively spring-like, the average February day is rather less enticing. A westerly gale with penetrating showers and a high wind-chill factor, or clammy drizzle, are more likely. These are the realities of daffodil picking, since the wetter the weather the faster the crop grows. So, clad in multi-coloured plastic coats and caps, protected by rubber gloves from the irritating daffodil sap, the pickers brave the elements for long hours, snapping the stems with both hands, banding them in tens, and carrying them to the end of the field. Here a 'checker' issues a ticket to credit them the agreed price per bunch, which is usually paid at the end of each day. Bunches must be kept clean, and the foreman checks to ensure that stems are at least 28 cm (11 in.) long. An upturn in the Cornish economy since the mid-1990s has reduced the numbers of local

Above: Modern bulb farms have replaced much manual labour with bins, each of which holds up to a tonne of bulbs. Below: The foreman checks the length of a bunch. Bunches must be at least 280 mm (11 inches) for export. Stem length can sometimes be insufficient at the beginning and end of the flowering season.

people who now take to the fields, and most pickers come from Eastern Europe, often as student parties or groups managed by labour providers, formerly known as gang masters. Several unfamiliar languages can be heard accompanying the snapping of stems.

Over a period of some 40 years, at the end of the twentieth century and early in the twenty-first century, it became noticeable that many of the early-growing varieties are flowering earlier. Early varieties have less need for autumn cold, and so are benefiting from the milder winters of recent years. Likewise in the Isles of Scilly, 'Paper White', 'Innisidgen' and even 'Soleil d'Or' are now flowering earlier.

3

Famous Names of Daffodils, Raisers and Growers

Famous daffodils

What makes for a famous plant name? Of course it needs to be well chosen, indicating someone or something great or excellent. The plant must be of real and lasting quality for it to become known and respected down the generations.

'Royal Sovereign', 'King Edward' and 'Victoria' are such names, and clearly carry the mark of greatness. The strawberry 'Royal Sovereign' has ceased to be widely grown, but the name lives on as a hallmark of quality and a reminder of a bygone age. Apple names such as 'Cox' and 'Bramley' also come to mind.

Such a name is 'King Alfred' which, in its day, was the ultimate daffodil. It has held centre stage in the industry and in the minds of the public for about 100 years, and is still sought even though production has dwindled. 'King Alfred' remains the one daffodil known to most people, and its enduring place as a great name underlines the British love of daffodils. How many other flowers have such a following?

Raised in Devon by John Kendall (1828–90), 'King Alfred' was launched about 1900, when it was awarded a First Class Certificate by the RHS, and priced at ten guineas (£10.50) a bulb. In 1902, Barr & Sons of Covent Garden listed it at £5.10 shillings each, a figure exceeded by only two other varieties in their extensive catalogue. It soon became recognized in Holland with a Forcing Award, and built a huge reputation over many decades.

The parentage of 'King Alfred' is obscure, it being described as a 'Maximus' hybrid. Its vigour and size are attributed to it acquiring a double set of chromosomes – an auto-tetraploid. However, the usual fate of all vegetatively maintained plant stocks is to decline in vigour as viruses invade, and this has inevitably been the fate of 'King Alfred', albeit the decline was rather slow. Today there are just a few acres remaining, its place on farms having long since been taken by 'Golden Harvest', which in Rosewarne trials yielded better and

For many years, 'Golden Harvest' has been the standard against which trumpet daffodils are measured.

'King Alfred' (above) was the number one daffodil before 'Golden Harvest'. Today, it is seldom seen, but the public remember it. It lives on in its double 'sport', 'Golden Ducat' (below).

flowered ten days earlier. Now, in its turn, 'Golden Harvest' is falling from favour due to its susceptibility to the basal rot fungus, a disease which 'King Alfred' resisted, except in the hotter states of the USA.

However, the 'King' lives on in its double-flowered form, 'Golden Ducat', which is a major cut-flower variety, especially in Cornwall. This was registered by Speelman & Sons in Holland, and is a fine, uniform flower, unlike some doubles which can revert to the single form. 'Golden Ducat' is not a good garden plant, since with heavy heads and weak stem it bows down for slugs to enjoy. Commercially, the flowers attract good prices but, as with most 'doubles', it fails to open if picked too early.

Although new daffodils never caused anything akin to Dutch 'Tulipomania' of the 1630s,

When 'Fortune' appeared in 1917, it caused a sensation. Today it is largely abandoned in hedgerows.

one well-known variety did cause a sensation when it appeared in 1917. 'Fortune', a yellow and orange Division 2 flower, is reported to have been sold by the raiser, Walter T. Ware of Bath, for £50 per bulb, and nine years later it was still priced at £17. 'Fortune' has received more awards than almost any other variety, and is still important today for early forcing. It was grown extensively in Cornwall, the bulbs often pre-cooled to advance flowering, and is still widespread in woods and abandoned plots in West Penwith. 'Fortune' has brittle stems and leaves, and is not a good choice for the garden.

Two famous names originating in Cornwall are the widely differing 'Carlton' and 'Tête à Tête'. 'Carlton', an all yellow, large-cupped daffodil, was a creation of P.D. Williams of Lanarth. The parentage was never recorded. At its peak, it was said to be the largest clonal plant in the world. This too has a double form, called 'Dick Wilden'. 'Tête à Tête', a miniature raised by Alec Gray of Camborne, is definitely a great name, and is now widely known due to the vast production in Holland. Description is scarcely necessary as it is on sale throughout the land. Its 'sisters', 'Jumblie' and 'Quince', are also exceptionally good miniature daffodils.

A shortlist of great names must include 'Magnificence' and 'Golden Harvest', leading trumpet daffodils of the past 75 years. 'Magnificence', like 'King Alfred', is described as a 'Maximus' hybrid. It was raised by the Revd George Engleheart in Hampshire, and registered before 1914. For decades it was the earliest daffodil in Cornwall and the Isles of Scilly, but it is seldom seen today.

'Golden Harvest' probably played a larger part in the expansion of the Cornish industry than any other daffodil. It was raised in Holland from 'Golden Spur' x 'King Alfred', and registered before 1920. It has many attributes – early flowering, high yielding, and suitable for pre-cooling, producing good quality flowers after hot-water treatment. It has a variable double-flowered form called 'Planet'. Today, basal rot-resistant replacements for 'Golden Harvest' are being sought, and Rosewarne's 'Kerensa', 'Emblyn' and 'Dellan' are increasing in acreage.

Finally, 'Grand Soleil d'Or' is a great name, and the mainstay of the Scillonian industry. It may have acquired the prefix 'Grand' when, long ago, it perhaps underwent a chromosome doubling. In the 1970s, virus disease threatened the crop, and scientists at the Littlehampton Research Station saved the day by producing virus-free plants.

Some notable Cornish daffodil growers and enthusiasts

The development of the Cornish daffodil industry occurred over a period of some 120 years, during which it attracted a number of talented and interesting people. These include growers, those in the bulb trade and the flower market, as well as research workers and advisers whose enthusiasm for the crop promoted it and helped build the industry we see today. A dynamic quartet in the second half of the twentieth century, were Bill Secrett OBE, Arthur Tomlin MBE, Charles Le Grice MBE and Dan du Plessis. Their irrepressible interest in daffodils created a very exciting atmosphere, and invariably generated a lively discussion at meetings at Rosewarne EHS.

Bill Secrett, son of F.A. Secrett, the greatly respected Thames Valley market gardener, followed in the business which his father had established in Truro between the two World Wars. There was a time when, to qualify as a horticulturist, it was almost mandatory to have trained at the Secrett Farm at Millford near Godalming in Surrey. It was therefore not surprising that Bill was well schooled in management, record-keeping and economics. Bill was very fair in all his dealings, but did like to get straight to the point. On occasions, during a telephone conversation, he might say, 'Now this is getting interesting, I am switching on the tape recorder.' This also happened with advisory colleagues, and there was no doubt that it concentrated the mind wonderfully. He assisted several other growers in taking up daffodil growing; chaired the Rosewarne EHS Committee from 1974 to 1979, and was awarded the OBE. On his retirement, Bill Secrett's farming interests in the Truro area were taken over by Maurice Crouch, of March, Cambridgeshire.

Arthur Tomlin, with his two brothers, Ralph and Geoffrey, started growing bulbs at Polgoon, Penzance in the 1920s, selling the business to Geest in 1973 when it moved to Varfell. The Tomlins were dedicated daffodil growers, always seeking to understand the crop and make improvements.

During the 1960s and 1970s, techniques were changing rapidly, and Arthur suspected a link between the increase in basal rot disease and the picking of first-year flowers. He suspected that roots were being broken as flowers were plucked from the recently planted bulbs. He experimented with copper dips, but the idea was quickly overtaken by the appearance on the market of benomyl (Benlate) and thiabendazole (Storite). Tomlin Brothers was the foundation upon which the Cornish branch of Winchester Growers was later established.

Charles Le Grice qualified as a solicitor, and worked in London, Totnes and Launce-

The Sou'westers Horticultural Club, established by Fred Shepherd, Rosewarne's first Director. Photo 1964. Members included the dedicated Bill Secrett (seated, third from left), Arthur Tomlin (seated, second from left) and Charles Le Grice (seated, second from right). (See page 144 for names of all founder members pictured.)

ston. Gradually moving west, he fulfilled an ambition to begin farming when he and his wife, Wilmay, were able to take over a family-owned farm on the outskirts of Penzance. Starting with dairy cows, anemones, violets and iris, he bought his first daffodil bulbs in 1955. His lively brain soon saw how to apply new information on producing very early flowers by pre-cooling the bulbs. How he enjoyed coming to Rosewarne waving a bunch of 'Hollywood' daffodils in mid-November! Charles was a champion of bud-picking and flower exports through the co-operative Lingarden, and was always eager to share any new observation or theory relating to daffodils.

Dan du Plessis, a daffodil grower at Landulph, Saltash, was a man for whom everyone in the daffodil world had enormous respect. This was not for the size of his business,

which he shared with his brother Peter, but for his knowledge and love of the crop, as well as the service that he gave to Rosewarne, the Daffodil Society and the Royal Horticultural Society (RHS) Daffodil Committee, over many years. Dan performed the invaluable role of acting as a bridge between the daffodil breeder and exhibitor, and the commercial grower. He was a constant supporter of all the daffodil shows in the South West, Birmingham and London, and achieved regular success for the quality and presentation of his flowers. As a keen naturalist, he also worked to help the local community and improve the environment of the Tamar Valley where he lived. A proud achievement was the award of the Peter Barr Cup in 1984 for his work on daffodils. His registrations included two double daffodils 'Gay Kybo' and 'Tamar Fire'. Latterly he took

Dan du Plessis (left), for whom everyone in the daffodil world had enormous respect, and Rudi Mock (right), who established one of the fastest growing daffodil businesses of recent times.

up daffodil breeding, his seedlings being taken on by his nephew, Ron Scamp.

During the tenure of the former Tomlin farm near Penzance by Geest in the 1970s, there were two exceptionally good managers in Jim Houghton and Stanley Pastuch. Jim had been immersed in bulb growing since a young man, and had risen through the ranks at J.T. White's in Spalding. Needing a new challenge, he came to Penzance in 1972 as manager, and became a staunch supporter of Rosewarne and its work. Jim improved the company's bulb stocks by applying a process of 'green stock selection', in which he selected the very best bulbs to create a 'mother stock'. Stanley Pastuch continued the good work until

his untimely death in 1984. In 1987 the company was purchased by the Hampshire-based Winchester Bulbs Ltd.

Also in the 1970s, another Hampshire company, Parker Farms, set up in Cornwall. Under the experienced hand of John Humphrey, they farmed daffodils very successfully on the Roseland Peninsula. At the start of the twenty-first century, John remains a very knowledgeable and respected voice in the bulb world, with many connections in Holland. Although retired, he continues to help several businesses that market under the banner of 'Cornish King', a trademark established for a range of horticultural products by Roger Whilding of the Agricultural Development

Jim Hosking produces probably the best range of commercial daffodils in the country.

and Advisory Service (ADAS). Parker Farms became assimilated by Angloflora under the directorship of Frank Rusman, and is now centred on modern premises near Tregony, managed by Jeremy Oatey.

One of the more remarkable personalities in the daffodil industry is Rudi Mock MBE who, as a German prisoner of war, was sent to work on farms in Cornwall. His story is recounted in his book *Cornish Rhapsody – from a penny-halfpenny an hour to a fortune.* In 1948 he chose to stay in Cornwall and, with his wife Constance, built up, first with poultry and then daffodils, one of the fastest growing businesses of the times. When the new Rosewarne daffodils were offered for sale in the 1980s, Rudi, through the group known as Cornwall Area Bulb Growers' Association (CABGA), made a substantial contribution to

ensuring that Cornwall secured most of the stocks. Rudi had a progressive approach to business, and an eye for a potentially profitable variety. He was in the forefront of adopting bulk-bin bulb handling on his farm at Crowan.

Jim Hosking, farmer and daffodil enthusiast on the Tregothnan Estate, is a central figure in the National Farmers' Union (NFU) bulb forum, the Horticultural Development Council (HDC) bulb panel, and the Royal Show Committee, as well as many other important national bodies. Jim was Rosewarne chairman when closure loomed, and he worked tirelessly to try to save the station. Unfortunately, the 'near market' philosophy of the 1980s was an unstoppable force, which even Jim, at his most persuasive, supported by Steve Parsons, Principal of the Duchy College, could not halt. With his sons, Jeremy and James, he now pro-

Paul Clark (top) purchased the Tomlin/Geest Farm, near Penzance, naming it Winchester Bulbs. In 2000, he created a new bulb farm near Camborne. Rodney Ward (above), veteran Scillonian grower, as an exhibitor argued strongly against the move to bud picking.

duces what is probably the best range of commercial daffodil bulbs in the country, offering them for sale through the farm shop. Jim has generously donated bulbs to many charitable causes, and his bulbs brighten up Truro's Morlaix Avenue, and the Eden Project, each spring.

Coming right up to date, another leader in the daffodil world, Paul Clark, began farming at Winchester in Hampshire before moving into Cornwall with the purchase of the Geest farm at Varfell, creating the Penzance branch of Winchester Bulbs. In 1990, he sold Varfell to a management team under Dr Gordon Flint, and moved to Nocton in Lincolnshire. Returning to Cornwall with the purchase of Pendarves Farm, Camborne, in 2000, he has re-established a major presence in the county, based upon large-scale, low-cost production. He is a dedicated daffodil grower, who loves the crop and enjoys growing it efficiently.

The next two notable personalities were doyens of the bulb industry, but in different fields. Rodney Ward MBE (1904–2004), veteran Scillonian flower grower, and Carlo Naef OBE (1900–1997), former director of leading Covent Garden flower salesmen J. & E. Page, witnessed an era of massive change. First and foremost they were both daffodil enthusiasts, each seeking to promote and improve the crop, but their views on one particular aspect differed to the extent that they argued their respective corners on every occasion they met. The issue was the marketing of daffodils in bud.

Rodney farmed Normandy Farm on St Mary's, following in the footsteps of his father and grandfather. He was a leading grower and exhibitor, taking his flowers to London and many other shows. His love of daffodils gave him an indelible picture of what a fully coloured, perfectly formed daffodil should be. He contended that a daffodil picked in tight bud could never develop its full colour and quality. Carlo stated, equally forcefully, that unless the product changed it would never reach the wider public, and attempts to export it would be doomed. We now know that Carlo's argument won the day, although there are still some misgivings about the extremes to which the industry has gone. Of course, Rodney was also right. To obtain a show bloom, an exhibitor will always prefer to delay picking at least until the bud has begun to open.

Rodney named several varieties, including 'Mando', an early, golden daffodil, and 'Avalanche', a vigorous, bicoloured tazetta. Carlo, on a visit to Cornwall just after the Second World War, visited Michael Williams at Lanarth, and acquired a few bulbs of 'St Keverne', from which Geest eventually established a stock, marking a new era in the development of the crop.

A Dutchman, Matthew Zandbergen (1903–90), loved daffodils and, it is said, all things English. He visited Cornwall and the Isles of Scilly frequently, and helped many people. He was a businessman in the very best tradition, with an eye for a good daffodil. Perhaps the word 'scout' would not be inappropriate – a description he would have understood, as a resistance fighter in occupied Holland during the Second World War. Matthew probably played a part in the rise of 'Tête à Tête'. It would be interesting to know when he first saw Alec Gray's famous plant. As a roving ambassador for the bulb industry, he may have taken it to Holland and beyond. Dutchmen are well known for their entrepreneurial approach to international trade, including commercializing new and interesting plants. Britain has a long tradition in plant hunting, but would it be provocative to suggest that our passion for plants may sometimes have been driven more by academic interest and pride in possession than by commerce?

Finally, a selection of notable personalities would need to include Walter Abbiss and Don Horton. Abbiss (1893–1967) played a major part in creating order in the early days of the Cornish industry. Experimental work, commercial shows, marketing initiatives and development projects were pursued with great determination in his role as Horticultural Superintendent for Cornwall from 1923 to 1963. Among his many achievements, Abbiss is credited with introducing the anemone crop to Cornwall, improving winter cauliflower (broccoli) stocks, and establishing a co-operative hot-water tank at Gulval in 1926, which operated for over 30 years, and doubtless saved many businesses from extinction by eelworm (see Chapter 4, 'Eelworm, the daffodil plague'). In the 1967 RHS *Daffodil Yearbook*, Alec Gray praised Abbiss's enthusiasm and drive, adding, 'It will be a very long time before Cornwall knows his like again.'

Don Horton conducted bulb trials in both Cornwall and Lincolnshire. He became greatly respected in the industry, and by learning Dutch was able to introduce much bulb technology into Britain. He promoted rules for treating bulbs, and described the initiation of the flower bud in summer.

Famous Cornish daffodil breeders

Cornish enthusiasm for daffodils is reflected in the achievements of famous breeders who have devoted their lives to enhancing the beauty and commercial value of their favourite flower. No account of daffodil growing would be complete if it failed to mention three in particular: Percival Dacres Williams (1865–1935), Alec Gray (1895–1986), and Barbara Fry, BEM (1922–1997). The work of these three breeders

Percival Dacres – 'P.D.' – Williams (left), and his daffodil 'Carlton' (right), one of the most important standard daffodils raised in Cornwall, and perhaps the world's largest 'clonal' plant.

spans the whole life of the industry, and their achievements are recognized world-wide.

P.D. Williams (often known simply as P.D.) was a member of the wealthy Williams family that is particularly associated with camellias. His cousin, J.C. Williams of Caerhays, also a daffodil breeder, created hardy hybrids from *Camellia saluenensis*, so releasing them from the cosseted constraints of the conservatory to enjoy their universal popularity as a garden shrub.

From his home at Lanarth, St Keverne, on the Lizard Peninsula, P.D. poured forth a stream of wonderful daffodils from 1895 until his death in 1935 at the age of 70. Every commentator since then has acknowledged the quality of his varieties, it being said that in an unlabelled collection of daffodils it would not be difficult to pick out those of P.D.'s raising.

Their commercial importance is exemplified by the variety 'Carlton', registered before 1927 and yet still one of the most important daffodils. Another universally applauded variety is 'St Keverne', named after the village on the Lizard. Probably raised by P.D., 'St Keverne' was named and registered by his son Michael in 1934. A refined variety, it is one of the finest for gardens, being sturdy and basal-rot resistant. The rise and fall of 'St Keverne' is described in Chapter 5. Many of the Williams' varieties were given Cornish place-names – in fact, like Cornishmen, you will know them by the prefixes, 'Tre-', 'Pol-', and 'Pen-', a total of 73 such names plus 24 'Saints'.

Another important variety, 'California', is known as 'Pentewan' in Scilly, while others like 'Brunswick', 'Scarlet Elegance', 'St Agnes'

'California' (left) is among a host of very durable varieties raised by P.D. Williams.
'Trousseau' (right) is one of his finest flowers. It shows wonderful refinement for its time.

and the lovely 'Trousseau' were prominent for decades, but are tending to slip into obscurity. P.D. and Michael registered only the very best progeny with examples in all the daffodil divisions, including garden varieties like 'Beryl' and 'Jack Snipe', jonquils, 'Tresamble' and 'Trevithian', poetaz, 'Cragford' and 'Scarlet Gem', and the superior poet 'Lady Serena'.

P.D. was both a member and Vice-Chairman of the RHS Daffodil Committee; a man described in the 1936 yearbook as, 'courageous, wise, witty, kindly, of discriminating taste and content with nothing second best'. An authority on daffodils throughout the first decades of the twentieth century, he received the VMH and other awards for his achievements.

Alec Gray is associated with wonderful miniature daffodils. Alec was not only a horticulturist of wide experience, but an amateur archaeologist and poet. His working life began after the First World War, when he qualified in fruit growing and worked in North Devon. He became manager of the Gulval Experimental Station, Penzance, where he worked under Walter Abbiss, the County Adviser, before moving to the Isles of Scilly to manage the Duchy Farm. This was where his love of the Islands and miniature daffodils was kindled. By 1927, he had assembled a collection of narcissus species and varieties, including many of the tazetta group, which he began to hybridize. In 1937, he moved to Devoran, near Truro, where he registered his first seedling stocks and then, moving to Treswithian near Camborne, he raised a range of exceptionally neat 'miniatures' until 1984. On his retirement,

Alec Gray (above left) raised wonderful miniature daffodils. 'Segovia' (above right), registered in 1962, and 'Tête à Tête' (below), registered in 1949, his greatest achievement, which eclipsed all other dwarf varieties.

Alec Gray's collection was sold to Walter Stagg and thence to Lady Skelmersdale at Broadleigh Gardens, Taunton, where many still reside and continue to appear at spring shows at the RHS London Headquarters at Vincent Square, and elsewhere. He was revered at the RHS Daffodil Committee, which awarded him the Peter Barr Cup in 1945, and ten years later his book *Miniature Daffodils* was published.

Whenever Alec and his wife Flomay had a successful bulb season, their particular passion was to hasten over to Spain to seek yet more miniature treasures. Acquaintance with Alfred Tait, and later his niece, Muriel, of Oporto, Portugal, led to an exchange of bulbs in which Alec acquired a bulb of 'Cyclataz'. As the name implies, this is a hybrid between *Narcissus cyclamineus* and a tazetta, 'Soleil d'Or'. In Alec's hands, seed from this plant resulted in the ubiquitous little daffodil 'Tête à Tête'. The double play on words here is a classic, with Tait to Tait being transformed into French to describe the two flowers commonly found on each stem. Alec and Flomay received not a fraction of the fortune that 'Tête à Tête' has amassed, but in its time it may have helped finance some trips to Spain. First offered in 1956 at five shillings a bulb, the price doubled following the award of a First Class Certificate for pot culture in 1962. Dutch 'scouts' were not slow to recognize this, and its meteoric rise began. Today, with 585 hectares in Holland, it represents 34 per cent of Dutch production, and is to be found in millions of small pots throughout the world. Alec Gray's other important miniatures include 'Jumblie', 'Quince', 'Minnow', 'Baby Moon', 'Sun Disc' and 'April Tears'.

The third famous Cornish breeder was Barbara Fry BEM, whose work is described more fully in Chapter 5, 'Rosewarne Experi-

Barbara Fry, whose work for the daffodil will long be remembered.

mental Horticulture Station and its satellites'. As a civil servant, her brief was to raise taller and earlier-flowering daffodils for the trade. Now, some four decades later, we can claim that these aims have been brilliantly met, and through the co-operation of the growers, Cornwall has been successful in acquiring almost all of her best material.

Barbara was born in Gloucestershire in 1922, and came to work in Cornwall first as a Land Army Girl, and then with Mrs Doris Long of Trenoweth Valley Flower Farm, St Keverne. She joined the Rosewarne staff in 1958 as a field assistant, becoming assistant recorder and then scientific officer in 1979.

Barbara, affectionately known as 'Bob', possessed such dedication and a love of daffodils that she was entrusted with the daffodil collection, known as OP8, and later the daffodil-breeding brief. Rosewarne's narcissus variety trial reports became widely sought after, and when breeding work began in 1964 she was armed with a huge amount of information to assist her in selecting suitable parent stocks. Barbara retired in 1983, but continued some contract work until the Station closed in 1989. Her work was recognized with the award of the British Empire Medal in 1973, the RHS Peter Barr Cup in 1974, and the Veitch Medal in 1978. The American Daffodil Society awarded her its Gold Medal in 1981. Dan du Plessis, grower and daffodil expert, paid her a fitting tribute: 'Her work for the daffodil will be long remembered and the Cornish industry has a lot to thank her for.'

Dr R.V. Favell pursued his hobby of breeding daffodils in the Penberth Valley west of St Buryan until his death in 1936. Penberth is one of the most picturesque spots in West Cornwall, possessing a timeless tranquillity and purity of light. The valley contains small fields and hedges belonging to a bygone age when violets were in fashion. Little by little, nature has reclaimed the land, although plots of daffodils, Kaffir lilies and Watsonia still thrive there.

Dr Favell's most important commercial flower was 'Finland', an early bicolour trumpet. 'Sweetness', 'Logan Rock', 'Porthchapel' and 'Suzy' are numbered among his scented jonquils. Some of his seedlings were developed by Doris Long of Trenoweth Valley Flower Farm at St Keverne. Dr Favell's granddaughter, Lady Frances Banham, maintains a collection of the Penberth varieties.

A breeder may produce many new varieties, but with the passing of time, perhaps only one or two survive. In the case of E. Martin of Truro, just one is enough to ensure the raiser's immortality. 'Silver Chimes', a tazetta-triandrus hybrid, was considered to be such a lovely flower that it was selected for the special cleaning-up treatment by the Government laboratory at Littlehampton. By creating a virus-free stock, 'Silver Chimes' lives on, especially on the Isles of Scilly. It is a flower of great charm and purity.

Raising a new daffodil

Raising a new daffodil is surprisingly easy. Simply dab the pollen from one flower on to the stigma of another; allow the seedpod to develop; sow the seeds in autumn, and wait five years while the plants grow to flowering size. Such is the complexity of daffodil genetics that each resulting seedling will be unique – different from any other daffodil that ever existed. Some may give cause for much personal pride but, sadly, few are likely to be notable and therefore worth registering with a name.

The serious breeder needs clear objectives, such as producing a daffodil that is early or late, tall, dwarf or scented. Other aims might be a red, pink or banded cup, and suitable parents will be selected accordingly. Before making the cross-pollination, the anthers will be removed (emasculation) from the parent which will bear the seed (female), thus avoiding the possibility of self-pollination. It is important to record exactly what has been done as there will be a five-year wait before the resultant flower is seen. If any of the new seedlings show promise, these can be used to make further cross-pollinations (back-crosses). This has the effect of concentrating the favourable genes so that the required plant is gradually achieved. Above all, the breeder requires endless patience, an unwavering plan, and a systematic approach. It is best to start early in life!

However, not all successful daffodil breeders have taken a scientific approach. Luck can play a part. A case in point is that of the little-known variety 'Cyclataz', from which, as we have seen, came the three famous varieties 'Tête à Tête', 'Jumblie' and 'Quince'.

Raising new daffodils is not difficult, but the stamens must be removed (above left) to avoid self-pollination. Careful labelling (above right) is essential in order to assess results when the new plants first flower. New, high-quality varieties can command a high price for a while (right).

When plants in the seedbed reach flowering age, those that show promise need to be isolated, and since each plant is different, each will need a title. Most breeders adopt a code number. For example, 'Tamara', the first daffodil registered by Rosewarne, was originally known as 64/48/1. This cross between 'Trenance' and 'Rijnveld's Early Sensation' was made in 1964; it was the forty-eighth cross made that year and, when it flowered, was the first plant selected from that cross.

When a seedling of real quality has been produced, it needs to be propagated to create a clonal stock – a batch of identical

Daffodil seeds (top left) must be collected in mid-summer, before the capsule (top right) splits. Chipping bulbs (mid-left) to multiply the stock began in the 1980s, and is now mechanized (mid right). Twin-scaling (bottom) is a hand operation. It results in more but smaller young plants, which need growing on more carefully.

Ron Scamp of Falmouth (left) is one of Britain's leading daffodil breeders. Mark Vandervliet (right) moved from Jersey to Cornwall. His New Generation Growers is one of several companies that seeks new varieties and bulks them up.

plants that can be named and registered with the RHS. Bulbs are propagated by cutting them into pieces by techniques known as chipping or twin-scaling. This is generally not attempted until the hybrid has split up naturally into, say, six bulbs, when perhaps three can be safely propagated. Provided the new variety maintains its promise, the raiser may seek to sell some of the new clone by making it known on the show-bench.

Currently, in the early twenty-first century, prices for a winner may reach £10 to £20 per bulb, and in addition to winning trophies the bulb may be sought by other breeders.

It takes a long time for a new variety to amass the tonnage required by commercial growers. The route from breeder to broad commercial acres is an uncertain one. Many show daffodils are quite rapidly superseded and fade into obscurity, while some excellent-looking daffodils may be seen on the show-bench for years before being 'spotted' and adopted by commercial growers. The late Matthew Zandbergen and Dan du Plessis played such a role. Today, Johnny Walkers of Taylor's Bulbs; Mark Vandervliet of New Generation Growers, and Dutchman Jan Pennings provide a link between the breeders and commercial production. Ron Scamp, nephew of Dan du Plessis, is one of the country's leading daffodil breeders.

Daffodils, narcissi and the Royal Horticultural Society (RHS)

The final word in the naming and classification of daffodils lies with the RHS. With the help of its Daffodil Committee, it publishes and updates a register of over 25,000 names.

The Royal Horticultural Society conducts trials at Wisley, and makes awards to varieties that merit it.

It decides which new names are acceptable, rules on classification (Division) and, after trials at Wisley, makes awards to those that merit it.

The RHS maintains that whatever their size and shape, all are daffodils. However, many members of the public tend to make a distinction between daffodils – the large ones – and narcissi, the small, delicate, scented ones. This opinion seems to be deeply rooted but does provoke the question, 'What is the difference between a daffodil and a narcissus?'

Narcissus, the correct term for the whole genus, has two possible derivations. One is from the Greek myth in which Narcissus, a youth infatuated by his reflection in a pool, pines away on realizing that he could never love anyone else. The other, given by E.A. Bowles in his book *The Narcissus*, states that the Greek myth was rejected by Philemon Holland in 1601. He links the word narcissus with narcotic, a plant substance which 'betokeneth nummedness and dulnesse of sense'. The Greek word *narkissos*, probably from *narke* meaning numbness, is accepted as the most likely origin. Not only is the scent of certain narcissi heavy and oppressive, but the bulbs contain complex alkaloids. One chemical, when refined, called galanthamine (also found in snowdrops – *Galanthus*), is being used to check the onset of Alzheimer's disease. The variety 'Carlton' is the best source of galanthamine. Unlike tulips, which were eaten by the impoverished Dutch during the Second World War, daffodils are unpalatable and toxic.

'Daffodil' has an even more obscure origin. It is suggested that Asphodel, a plant which the ancient Greeks associated with the mythological Elysian fields where heroes enjoyed life after death, became associated with the daffodil. It seems that this came about more because of the sound of the two words than because of any marked similarity between the two plants, except that both are of Mediterranean origin, have yellow or white flowers and narrow, greyish-green leaves.

The RHS maintains the definitions of the 13 divisions of daffodils, as shown in the chart below, and in Appendix 7 (page 137). Each variety has the division number followed by Y, W, O or R, etc., which refer to the colours of the flower parts. For example, 'Golden Harvest' (Division 1) 1Y-Y has yellow petals (perianth) and a yellow trumpet. Although petals are usually of one colour, the cup may have bands of different colours. These are indicated by three letters in sequence from the inside of the flower; for example, 'Rainbow' 2W-WWP, which is overall white with a pink rim.

Some of the 13 divisions are illustrated in the photographs on pages 66–7.

RHS Daffodil Classification

	Division	Description
	Division 1	Flowers whose trumpet is longer, or as long, as the petals. An important group, generally considered to be a true daffodil, although, strangely, it derives from *Narcissus pseudonarcissus*, the 'Bastard Daffodil', or Lent Lily. Includes 'Golden Harvest' 1Y-Y and 'Dutch Master' 1Y-Y, which have superseded 'King Alfred' 1Y-Y and 'Magnificence' 1Y-Y. Growers are eagerly seeking newcomers to this group which will be resistant to basal rot disease. White trumpet daffodils, 1W-W and 1W-Y, tend not to be as popular commercially, and some white daffodils are especially prone to basal rot disease.
	Division 2	Large-cupped daffodils, whose cup (or corona) is more than one-third, but less than equal to the length of the petals. The leading commercial Division 2 varieties have been 'Carlton' 2Y-Y and 'California' 2Y-Y. There are many colour combinations, but important commercial ones have been 'Fortune' 2Y-O, 'Armada' 2Y-O and 'Red Devon' 2Y-O. 'Ice Follies' 2W-W is rightly popular, and the pinkish-tinged 'Salome' 2W-PPY is increasing in popularity.
	Division 3	Flowers have a cup of not more than one-third the length of the petals, and some of the brightest colours and contrasts of any daffodil. These characteristics are inherited from their poet parents. Examples are 'Barrett Browning' 3WWY-O and 'Winifred van Graven' 3W-YYR. 'After All' 3W-YYR is a brilliantly coloured May flower.

	Division	Description
	Division 4	Includes all double daffodils, whether they have one or more flowers per stem. 'Golden Ducat' 4Y-Y, 'Tamar Fire' 4Y-R and 'White Lion' 4W-WYY are examples of the former; 'Cheerfulness' 4W-Y has several scented flowers per stem.
	Division 5	Varieties possess the characteristics of *Narcissus triandrus*. Medium-sized daffodils with graceful form. 'Hawera' 5Y-Y, raised in New Zealand, is a delicate yellow flower with a number of nodding heads. Cornish-raised 'Tresamble' 5W-W and 'Thalia' 5W-W have a simple charm. 'Ice Wings' 5W-W is a more recent introduction.
	Division 6	Flowers have the instantly recognizable swept-back petals of *Narcissus cyclamineus*. The popular 'February Gold' 6Y-Y, 'Jet Fire' 6Y-O, 'Jenny' 6W-W and 'Dove Wings' 6W-Y are examples of shorter daffodils for the smaller garden. The last two named, raised by Cyril Coleman of Kent, are among many excellent dwarf varieties he produced. Some of the dwarf varieties in this group maintain their capacity to flower over many years.
	Division 7	The jonquils. They show the characteristics of the species, *Narcissus jonquilla*. They are multi-headed and beautifully scented. 'Suzy' 7Y-O and 'Sweetness' 7Y-Y, raised in Cornwall, and the prolific new variety 'Martinette' 7Y-O from Rosewarne are examples.
	Division 8	The tazettas. This division is in two parts. The 'true' tazettas, such as 'Paper White' 8W-W, 'Soleil d'Or' 8Y-O, and the vigorous 'Avalanche' 8W-Y, are closer to the original species than poetaz kinds like 'Cragford' 8Y-O and 'Geranium' 8Y-O which, as their group name suggests, are hybrids between poets and tazettas. The practical consequence of this is that bulbs of most poetaz varieties need winter cold, whereas the 'true' tazettas do not. 'Geranium' mutated to produce the double-flowered 'Sir Winston Churchill', which is therefore classed as 4W-O (not 8W-O).

	Division	Description
	Division 9	The 'Poets'. Late flowering, and with a fine scent. The flowers have pure white petals with a 'pheasant's eye' centre, and were once grown on a large scale, especially the variety 'Horace' 9W-GOR. Few poets are grown commercially today; their bulbs are rather unattractive and their stems and buds thin. 'Actaea' 9W-YYR is now the best-known poet.
	Division 10	*Narcissus bulbocodium*, or Hoop petticoat daffodils, native of the high Pyrenees. This group have never hybridized freely, and tend to remain aloof in the Alpine greenhouse or freely drained rock garden.
11a 11b	Division 11	Split corona daffodils. These were controversial when they first appeared, but new forms have come to be much admired. Dutchman Jack Gerritsen produced these over many years. Recently others have taken up the challenge of producing these flamboyant flowers. 'Baccarat' 11aY-Y, 'Orangery' 11aW-OOY, and the large-flowered 'King Size' 11aY-Y, are examples of sub-group (a), classed as Collar daffodils. Others, known as Papillon daffo-dils, are in sub-group (b), and have less overlapping, smaller corona segments.
	Division 12	Represents a recent change in classification, and accommodates hybrids that span several groups. Varieties of greatest interest here include 'Tête à Tête' 12Y-Y and its sisters 'Jumblie' 12Y-O and 'Quince' 12YY. 'Cornish Chuckles' 12Y-Y produces several stems per bulb, which extends the flowering period, and could become a popular dwarf variety.
	Division 13	Comprises daffodils known only by their botanical name, such as the diminutive *Narcissus cyclamineus* and *N. pseudonarcissus* and its variants, including *N. obvallaris*, the Tenby Daffodil.

Left: A modern jonquil hybrid (Division 7) still retains the characteristics of Narcissus jonquilla.
Right: Narcissus *var. 'Tahiti'. All double-flowered daffodils are placed in Division 4.*

Left: 'Jet Fire', an American cyclamineus hybrid (Division 6) has become very popular.
Right: 'Peeping Tom' has all the characteristics of the cyclamineus group (Division 6).

Left: Daffodils which do not fit the definition of any other division, such as 'Cornish Chuckles', are placed in Division 12. Right: Miniature daffodils of the bulbocodium group (Division 10) do not hybridize freely, so tend to remain aloof in the Alpine greenhouse or well-drained rock garden.

Left: Narcissus *var. 'Rainbow' (Division 2). Middle:* Narcissus triandrus *(Division 5).*
Right: Tazetta narcissus 'Paper White' (Division 8).

Left: 'Golden Dawn' (Division 8, but with definite jonquil characteristics) marks the end of the Scillonian season. Middle: 'Martinette' came from the USA via Rosewarne. A jonquil hybrid, it is admired for its fine scent. Right: A subsection of Division 8 are poetaz varieties – crosses between tazettas and poets.

4

Trials and Tribulations

Eelworm, the daffodil plague

In April 1917 the young industry found itself reeling under the effects of a plague that had been devastating crops for more than ten years, and for which there appeared to be no cure. The RHS cancelled its daffodil shows due to the depressed state of the growers, and with a fear akin to that caused by a more recent outbreak of Foot and Mouth Disease, there was a state of paralysis in the industry. The plague, whatever it was, had first appeared some 30 years earlier, but now plants were dying and bulbs rotting in increasing numbers.

For want of a name, the new affliction was called the 'rootless disease'. The hope was that it would pass; some suggested it was due to waterlogging, or perhaps to an ill-defined vapour in the earth. Much the same had been said about Potato Blight some 50 years earlier, until Anton DeBary discovered the blight fungus in 1861.

As the situation worsened, hundreds of acres of daffodils were being wiped out, with growers facing ruin. Mr Alec Wilson, a friend of P.D. Williams, was so disheartened that he gave up daffodil growing altogether when the value of his stocks fell from £12,000 to less than £200 in two seasons. P.D. Williams first saw the trouble in 1901, and thought it was caused by the numerous narcissus fly grubs in the rotten bulbs. Interestingly, he also reported that affected bulbs contained mites and eelworms.

It was E.J. Welsford and J.K. Ramsbottom who confirmed that a microscopic nematode, *Ditylenchus dipsaci*, discovered by the German Kühn on teasels in 1858, was responsible for the 'rootless disease'. Under its present name of Stem and Bulb Nematode, it is still very much with us today.

Nematodes are one of the most numerous and diverse forms of life, with incredible powers of reproduction and survival. The need to control them affects everything the bulb grower does. The presence of narcissus fly maggots

A rolling inspection table enables unhealthy bulbs to be picked off.

James Kirkham Ramsbottom (above) began his study of eelworm at Wisley in 1916, and within two years devised the hot-water cure – just in time to save the young industry from destruction. Stem and bulb eelworm, the bane of daffodil growers, reveals its presence by brown rings in the bulbs (below).

and mites in affected bulbs was later shown to be explained by the attraction that rotting, eelworm-infested bulbs hold for other scavengers. Like little vultures, they home in on carcasses in the vicinity.

The eelworm epidemic continued unabated during and after the First World War because of neglect and the priority given to food production. Farm and garden workers were called to the Western Front never to return – events chronicled in Tim Smit's *The Lost Gardens of Heligan*. Then, following restrictions on flower growing, there was a rush to expand, with the inevitability of diseased bulbs being traded and dispersed throughout England and Holland. Bulbs with a light eelworm infestation can appear reasonably normal, perhaps showing just a few pale raised bumps on the leaves (known as spickels), but in the following summer, the pest multiplies rapidly, rotting the bulb and migrating to other bulbs, the soil, buildings and equipment. Towards the end of the war, a conference was called, which led to the decision by the RHS and some leading growers to sponsor an investigation into the biology and control of daffodil eelworm. The task was given to a 25-year-old Wisley student, James Kirkham Ramsbottom, who pioneered the use of hot-water treatment.

It is reported that hot-water dipping was first used to kill narcissus fly maggots in 1911, so the idea was not totally new to Ramsbottom, but even so his achievements in just two seasons were remarkable. In this short time he demonstrated that a four-hour soak in water at 43.3° C (110° F) killed eelworm (see also Chapter 5, 'A nice warm bath'). He repeated his findings on commercial stocks at Spalding and, in 1919, supervised the treatment of 2,000 seedling stocks belonging to P.D. Williams. His intervention may well have saved many varieties, including 'Carlton'. In 1924, Ramsbottom was awarded the Peter Barr Memorial Cup for his pioneering work. His fame spread to the USA, where he undertook a lecture tour in 1925. Tragically, while in New York, he died at the age of 33. Had he lived, one wonders what else he might have achieved. It has been rightly said that he saved the daffodil industry, and his findings will live as long as there is a bulb industry.

In 1930, it was realized that another step forward was needed to support the growing bulb industry. Lincolnshire County Council took the lead by establishing an Experimental Station at Kirton, near Boston, as a national centre for bulb research and advice. However, since conditions in Cornwall differ from those in Lincolnshire, Cornwall County Council followed suit and created its own centre at Gulval, Penzance. Later, the Kirton site and Rosewarne became MAFF experimental stations serving the two major bulb-growing areas.

Subsequent studies on daffodil eelworm and control measures built up a picture of an incredibly successful and persistent organism. A MAFF nematologist colleague once declared that the behaviour of daffodil eelworm owed more to fiendish conspiracy than to respectable evolution. Ramsbottom's trials of the early twentieth century remain the basis of nematode control in daffodil bulbs but, despite the advances made, the pest remains the number one enemy of the grower, requiring constant vigilance.

Merodon, the narcissus fly

There are two kinds of narcissus fly. Small Fly, and Large Fly, or *Merodon*. Both have a larval (maggot) stage which feeds in daffodil bulbs, but the Small Fly, once thought to be very serious, we now know to be a scavenger, attacking only those bulbs which have already been damaged by some other means. It lays many eggs, and the sight of a partly rotten bulb crawling with maggots does explain the concern with which earlier generations of bulb growers viewed it.

However, the real villain is Large Narcissus Fly. This handsome, hairy, brown insect, slightly smaller than a bee, dashes about in summer with a purposeful buzz, laying just one egg against each plant. Despite its small size, the newly hatched maggot has powerful jaws with which to chew into the tough base of the bulb, until it reaches the nutritious embryo flower in the centre. Here, it feeds voraciously until the following spring, growing into a fat grub wallowing in its own excreta ('frass' in polite quarters). The bulb is invariably ruined.

Large Narcissus Flies are on the wing in May, June and part of July, whenever the weather is warm and sunny. This southern species, near the edge of its range in the UK, is commonest in the South West, and the increase in daffodil growing and trading in the first half of the twentieth century, before the advent of insecticides, assisted its spread.

There are some amusing accounts of attempts to catch the flies with butterfly nets, and no doubt the more nimble growers and their staff achieved some success. The trick was to creep up on the fly in the morning when the adults were still cold and drowsy. Other means were tried, including netting over the more valuable beds, or putting out baits or sprays of syrup and arsenic. It seemed that the only way to ensure that a bulb was not harbouring the hated maggot was to look closely at its base where a small scar would show where the young grub had entered.

Soon after the Second World War, the potent insecticides, DDT, aldrin and dieldrin

Merodon, the Large Narcissus Fly *(top), vies with vine weevil as one of the gardener's most hated pests. The handsome, hairy brown insect lays just one egg against each plant. Bulbs (above) are invariably ruined.*

became available. Incorporating aldrin dust into potting compost was highly effective against vine weevil, and the author can vouch for this: when he had care of large batches of cyclamen, there was not a sign of vine weevil in thousands of pots. Aldrin and dieldrin achieved the same success against narcissus fly, and the effect of a single treatment lasted for several years. During the 1960s, experiments showed that bulbs could be dipped in the insecticide before planting, or it could be applied as a spray in the planting furrows. Growers may look back, perhaps somewhat enviously, to the 30 years during which Narcissus Fly was under complete control in commercial crops.

Recognition that the modern insecticides were just too potent soon followed. In 1963, Rachel Carson's book *Silent Spring* signalled a wake-up call to the world. These compounds were shown to persist in the soil, in small organisms, birds, mammals and people, becoming more concentrated and damaging as they moved up the food chain. The use of aldrin was permitted on bulbs for longer than on most other crops by means of a European Community derogation because there was no alternative for bulb fly control. Its limited use on an ornamental crop such as daffodils was considered to be of little risk to the environment. Conservationists were not convinced, and it seems that they have since been vindicated by the increase in birds of prey and otters following the total ban. When in 1989 the Newlyn River, near Penzance, was found to be contaminated with insecticide, the ban was immediate. With the passage of time, it is easy to forget the conflict that followed the publishing of Rachel Carson's book, and the opposition to it presented by chemical companies and the farming lobby.

Throughout the 'Aldrin era', Narcissus Fly populations survived in gardens and wild places; and so, in the early years of the twenty-first century, with no really effective control measures, the industry still has a problem, albeit a less serious one than was predicted when the aldrin ban was first imposed. The present situation is best described as an uneasy truce. Currently, most daffodils are grown on large farms using rented land often remote from gardens and other daffodil fields. Early lifting – increasingly necessary to meet the requirements of bulb exporters – reduces fly attack by deterring the fly or killing the maggot before it can penetrate the bulb. Once bulbs are out of the ground they are safe from attack, but any maggot that has penetrated is killed by hot-water treatment (HWT).

Nevertheless, Large Narcissus Fly is still widespread, and can cause significant crop losses following warm summers. When temperatures rise above 20° C, the males become very active and defend their patch aggressively. With the prospect of climate change there is the possibility that the pest could increase both in numbers and range. Some recent research has been aimed at trying to understand what attracts the egg-laying female to the narcissus plant. Bulbs drying on the soil surface do not trigger the egg-laying response. The fly prefers to crawl down the crack in the soil beside the plant to deposit an egg near the bulb, where the young larva will stay moist. Some trials have shown that defoliating, or burning the leaf, can reduce attacks, possibly by confusing the fly in its quest for the host plant. However, not all trials have produced conclusive results.

Insidious mites

Yet another enemy of the daffodil grower is Bulb Scale Mite (BSM), *Steneotarsonemus*. This insidious pest has been a lurking menace for generations, because once present in a stock it tends to persist. Again, two kinds of mites can cause confusion. BSM is not normally the mite seen in huge numbers in rotten bulbs, which is more likely to be the Bulb Mite, *Rhizoglyphus*, a secondary invader. To detect BSM requires much closer inspection, as the bulb may appear sound, but when cut open reveals an infestation that shows as brown marks between the scales and in the neck region.

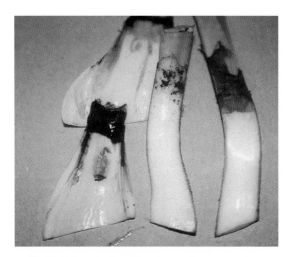

The insidious bulb scale mite continues to resist methods that should have eliminated it.

Here, the much smaller mites may be seen – oval, straw coloured, and accompanied by colourless eggs, slightly larger than the mites themselves. The mites' feeding between the scales and on the leaf and stem bases can severely distort subsequent growth, with stunted, curved leaves which may have a rough 'saw-edge'.

BSM has few other known hosts, and since it is killed by standard hot-water treatment it should have disappeared from commercial stocks by now. Studies are taking place to see whether it has other, as yet unknown, means of survival and spread. Mites breed most rapidly under warm conditions, and if infested bulbs are forced the crop can be ruined within a week or two. Long ago the best advice available was to return the boxes outdoors and hope for a frost that would kill most of the mites.

As with Narcissus Fly, climate change could favour the pest, and in recent years BSM has been observed to continue breeding throughout the Cornish winter. It is highly unlikely that any chemical treatments will become available to control this pest. Future, growers will have to combine knowledge of pest behaviour with cultural, hygiene and perhaps biological approaches.

Basal rot, the 100 years war

Between 1889 and 1900, frequent reference was made in the horticultural press to a disease that rotted daffodil roots and bulbs starting from the base. Known as basal rot, it has retained this name ever since. However, once again, there was confusion as to its cause. The disease could be seen first as a premature withering of the leaves, but more worrying was the tendency for an increasing number of bulbs to rot throughout the summer and autumn, after they had been dried, cleaned, or perhaps sold. Attacks seemed to vary from year to year, and the hot summer of 1911 brought huge losses in England and Holland. Was it another manifestation of eelworm, the 'rootless disease'?

With the benefit of hindsight we can understand the confusion at a time when eelworm was at its worst. Plant pathologists studying stocks with 'basal rot', which also contained eelworms, considered the latter to be the cause of the trouble, while others, perhaps studying eelworm-free bulbs, disagreed.

Eventually, a fungus, *Fusarium*, was confirmed as the cause – a genus of soil-inhabiting fungi which attack the roots of many crops throughout the world. Separate strains of the fungus attack different crops – one tomatoes, another carnations, yet another bananas. Even each bulb crop is host to its own strain; hence daffodil basal rot labours under the name of *Fusarium oxysporum forma speciale narcissi*.

Fusarium becomes more aggressive in warm soils, and this a major factor favouring the UK and especially Cornwall, since Cornish summers are seldom hot. For this reason, competition from hot Southern latitudes is unlikely.

Daffodil varieties vary considerably in their ability to resist *Fusarium* attack, and the industry is seeking the 'Holy Grail' of total resistance. Over the years, the disease has probably been a major factor in the disappearance of a large proportion of the 25,000 daffodils named since the mid-nineteenth century. Recent research confirms that there is no single gene for resistance or susceptibility; there are many, and so the inheritance of resistance is no simple matter. However, resistance in the variety 'St Keverne' has been studied, and shows that it produces barriers in the base plate when attacked. But to complicate matters, *Fusarium* can also enter the neck of the bulb, and all varieties can be affected in this way.

Many fungicides have been tested as bulb dips in the 100 years' war. Mercurial compounds were widely used until the middle of the twentieth century, when it was realized that they were dangerous, cumulative poisons. Then came Benlate, but its short life in solution meant that a dip required daily renewal. In the early twenty-first century, thiabendazole (Storite), a material that first appeared as a worming agent for cattle, is the favoured treatment. Recent research shows that it is more efficient if the dip is acidified with sodium bisulphate. The two major varieties most often treated are 'Golden Harvest' and 'Carlton'.

A susceptibility test devised at Rosewarne has helped to ensure that new varieties distributed from the station possess some disease resistance. In this test, a white daffodil, 'Moonstruck', was totally destroyed while 'St Keverne' survived. Growers in the Isles of Scilly have few concerns over basal rot because they grow mainly basal-rot resistant tazetta narcissi.

Today, the atmosphere of bulb stores is more accurately controlled, and a temperature no higher than 17° C is recommended, with

A healthy crop of daffodils (top), and an adjacent field, showing serious losses from basal rot (bottom).

Growers have waged war against basal rot for 100 years. It has probably caused the demise of thousands of varieties. Softness and a whitish mould on the base of the bulb reveal the presence of basal rot fungus (top). Infected bulbs (bottom).

Virus wars

Virus diseases are well known to every grower and gardener, but to former generations they must have been yet another unaccountable happening, causing a favourite plant to simply waste away. Viruses cause damage by plundering the host's proteins. However, there was the exceptional occasion when a virus enormously enhanced the value of a plant. This was when infection with the 'tulip-breaking virus' resulted in the bizarre colour patterns of 'Rembrandt' tulips. Some of the most exotic variants sold for huge sums of money in tulip-crazed Holland of the seventeenth century. This was, of course, long before the discovery of viruses.

Although in animals the immune system usually overcomes infection, plants retain viruses permanently. Seeds are generally virus free, but clonal stocks, raised year-on-year from the same vegetative material, perpetuate and accumulate viruses. There are at least 16 different virus diseases of daffodils, most of which are spread by sap-sucking aphids or soil nematodes.

There was one narcissus variety in which virus deterioration was viewed with such alarm that a national rescue programme was introduced to save it. This was 'Grand Soleil d'Or', mainstay of the Scillonian industry which, by 1970, was found to have become seriously weakened. Virologists at the Littlehampton Research Station confirmed the presence of Narcissus Degeneration Virus, an aphid-borne infection, and produced some virus-free plants by meristem culture in the laboratory. The new stock became known as 'Super Sol'. In trials it produced a higher yield, with larger and brighter coloured flowers.

Isles of Scilly growers continue to maintain a quarantine greenhouse of virus-free plants which are regularly propagated and distributed

temperatures in the 20°s avoided. A short period of 30° C or above, where this is needed, seems to cause little problem. Where growers adhere to this advice, the risk of disease is much reduced. Further factors that can help reduce attacks include avoiding hot, south-facing fields and, where possible, orientating ridges north to south.

Left: Plants infected with viruses gradually weaken and do not recover. They are best removed and burnt.
Right: Soil sickness is responsible for the root rotting in the poorer of the two plant samples.

to growers. Since the loss of so much of our publicly funded research base, it is doubtful whether such a 'cleaning up' operation would ever be repeated.

Combating 'soil sickness'

'Soil sickness' sounds like a biblical plague, or some massive pollution incident rendering the land useless. In reality it is not so bad, but for the grower it is something to be aware of or crops can fail to thrive, resulting in severe loss of income.

The scientific name for this malaise is Specific Replant Disease, caused by planting the same crop in the same place too often – in other words, not practising a rotation. Affected crops can be annuals or long-lived plants. Peas after peas, roses after roses, apples after apples – each can suffer the effects of 'soil sickness'.

Scillonian daffodil growers planting frequently on the same land suffer more than mainland farmers who regularly move to new land. The standard solution is to chemically fumigate the soil to prevent a build-up of the pathogens responsible, but a new and interesting possibility is to grow *Tagetes*, a type of French Marigold, as a 'break' crop. Trials show that this pungent plant can reduce certain pathogens in the soil, introducing a new word, 'bio-fumigation', to the vocabulary.

Soil injection with a fumigant (left) has been the sole means of combating soil sickness for many years. Soil sampling (right) and a laboratory test are used to detect nematodes which cause soil sickness in narcissus.

Surviving World Wars

The two World Wars impacted considerably on the flower and bulb industry. In 1914, production was rising, and farmer Reg Dobbs, in his book *Bulbs in Britain*, states that the infant bulb and flower business underwent a period of eclipse so that, by 1918, production had become severely limited by government regulations. With heavy losses of merchant shipping, and the diversion of much that remained into transporting war materials, the overwhelming priority was to increase home food production. Bulbs received little attention and were left to survive in odd corners unsuited to growing food. In the 1920s, there was a resurgence of both daffodil and tulip growing, and the strong post-war market led to major developments in bulb forcing, with 20 acres of new glasshouses

in the Spalding area. Following the eelworm crisis, the wider use of hot-water treatment put the industry back on a more secure footing.

Bulb growing flourished between the two World Wars, despite the general depression when most agricultural commodities suffered. Indeed, this was later remembered as a golden age of expansion, when many large companies became established. At Braunton, North Devon, Seymour Cobley Ltd. established a large unit. Their 1936 catalogue states:

> By far the greatest number of daffodils now in commerce have been raised in Great Britain. There are more of them grown here than in any other country, including Holland, and we believe ourselves to be the largest growers of them.

During this period, Tomlin Brothers and F.A. Secrett became established in Cornwall, while in Lincolnshire The Spalding Bulb Company, Verdegaal and others rose to prominence.

Much stricter limits were imposed on flower and bulb growing during the Second World War (1939–44). Reg Dobbs recalls how the government, having learnt lessons from the First World War, swung quickly into action with the creation of the County War Agricultural Executive Committees (known as 'War Ags'). The acreage of crops, machinery, fertilizer, fuel and labour were all controlled, with non-essential crops restricted and glasshouses used for tomatoes. A regulation in 1941 ordered a halving of Cornwall's 2,000 acres of flowers, and later this was reduced to 500 acres. However, some bulb exports to the USA were encouraged as shipping was largely empty in that direction and Holland, the only other source of bulbs, was under German occupation.

In November 1942, the Transport of Flowers Act came into force. This banned flowers from the railways and restricted road transport. The regulations represented a challenge that some were prepared to defy, especially since the implementation of transport rules seemed petty in the extreme, even applying to flowers concealed in luggage.

Some larger operators were arrested, and quite severe penalties imposed, including prison sentences of six and 12 months respectively for two London hauliers carrying 138 boxes of daffodils, violets and anemones. These were said to be worth between £2,000 and £3,000, figures which show that there was no lack of demand for flowers in war-torn Britain.

A timely, well-contrived initiative by Scillonian growers achieved some relaxation of the controls. They sent some scented narcissi to wartime Prime Minister Winston Churchill, who was sufficiently impressed by the gesture to declare, 'These people must be enabled to grow their flowers and send them to London – they cheer us up so much in these dark days.'

The rail ban was lifted on 18 March 1943, on condition that flowers did not occupy space required for essential war supplies. Cornish growers responded the very next day with 1,000 boxes, and seven and a half tons of flower boxes were shipped from the Scillies the following day.

Bulb stocks soon recovered, and the provisions of the 1946 Agriculture Act established a National Agricultural Advisory Service (NAAS, see also page 80), which began the process of improving husbandry and introducing new techniques. The industry again expanded and flourished in the 1950s and 1960s, but in the early 1970s production began to outstrip demand. Fortunately, a new initiative to export daffodil flowers and bulbs was taken by a growers' co-operative, Selected Growers, later renamed Lingarden. The co-operative effort received strong support from the industry, and Cornish bulbs were particularly favoured in the USA. In 1979 and 1981, British Bulb Exporters and MAFF jointly staged daffodil shows in Hillegom, Holland. The export trade has been a major factor in sustaining the industry ever since, although at times, currency fluctuations have created difficulties, resulting in an over-supply on the home market.

5

Research that Underpins the Industry

The heyday of bulb research

Over the 100 or so years of commercial daffodil growing, certain technical developments stand out. For instance, James K. Ramsbottom's demonstrations (1917–19) that soaking bulbs in hot water killed eelworms and other pests (see Chapter 4, 'Eelworm, the daffodil plague'). His finding came at a critical time for the industry, and hot-water dipping will probably continue to be vital to the production of healthy bulbs for as long as the industry survives.

In 1932, W.E. Hodson, an entomologist working in Cornwall, published a detailed account of the life cycle and behaviour of Narcissus Fly. His accounts are remarkable for his patient observations. For example, he declared that there was just one generation per year, and that the female invariably laid only one egg on each plant. Egg mortality was between 30 and 90 per cent, and was affected by drought or heavy rain, with the higher losses occurring if

the eggs were not placed below ground near the bulb. Hodson's reports are packed with information only acquired by close observation, reminiscent of those of French entomologist Jean Henri Fabré (1823–1915).

In 1938, P.H. Gregory, based at Seale Hayne College, Devon, published studies on the White Mould fungus. His work was funded jointly by MAFF and the Great Western Railway, an indication of the importance the railways attached to the flower trade in those days. Gregory studied the over-wintering fungal bodies on leaf debris, and found that they germinated early in the year as the daffodil shoots were emerging. This finding underpins the current use of protective fungicides applied before infection occurs.

The Agriculture Act of 1946 created a National Agricultural Advisory Service (NAAS), which later became the Agricultural Development and Advisory Service (ADAS),

Micropropagation and the production of virus-free plants from cultured meristems were important areas of research and development nationally. Photographed at Rosewarne.

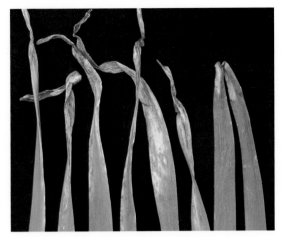 

Developments in the use of fungicides made great strides, and were important in the control of White Mould (left). Vase life and flower physiology studies made progress during the heyday (right).

and with it established a chain of regional experimental horticulture stations and husbandry farms. The Lincolnshire station at Kirton already existed, and was brought under the MAFF umbrella, while in Cornwall, Rosewarne EHS was established in 1951 on a new site at Camborne. Rosewarne had two satellite stations: Ellbridge, to study crops of the Tamar Valley, and the St Mary's sub-station, to assist the Islands' narcissus industry.

For about 30 years the advisory services provided free advice to any grower or farmer requesting it. Technical information was obtained from many sources, but was supplied mainly from work undertaken at the national research stations and regional experimental centres such as Rosewarne.

By 1960 there were nine experimental stations in England and Wales, and four horticultural research stations: East Malling, Long Ashton, Wellesbourne, and the Glasshouse Crops Research Institute at Littlehampton. There were also regional and sub-regional laboratories such as Westbury on the outskirts of Bristol, and Starcross, near Exeter. The research effort was well integrated, and the considerable amount of experimental work undertaken focused on practical solutions to problems.

Many of the scientists specializing in bulb technology were world leaders in their fields. Unfortunately, the heyday of bulb research was short lived. In the mid-1980s, support for research and free advisory services were withdrawn following a change of government policy, which expected 'near-market' research to be financed by industry. Large numbers of research posts disappeared, and Rosewarne EHS, the Starcross laboratory and the Littlehampton Research Station all closed.

However, during this brief period, much was achieved, and the industry prospered with good demand both at home and abroad. The improved control of leaf diseases and basal rot come high on the list of achievements. There were new daffodils from Rosewarne, and bulb physiologists studied forcing, crop density, aspects of stem length, post-harvest physiology and bulb storage. Virologists made huge strides, not only identifying the viruses of narcissi, but also in producing virus-free stocks. In parallel with this came the development of propagation techniques.

Although bulb research today is only a fraction of what it was 30 years ago, the industry appears to be quite buoyant, with most of the urgent research needs being funded by the industry through the Horticultural Development Council (HDC), which sponsors surveys and trials. The HDC grower panels decide on the priorities, but the sums available in the bulb sector are not large, and much less than in Holland. One consequence of this is the UK's much reduced participation in the international forum of bulb researchers.

Rosewarne Experimental Horticulture Station (EHS) and its satellites

Experimental Centres were set up by MAFF under the post-war Agriculture Act (1946) to boost production and provide a link between research and practice.

The Rosewarne site was acquired in 1951, with Fred Shepherd as its first Director. Sites from Penzance to the Devon–Dorset border were inspected before the choice of the 100-acre farm at Camborne was finally agreed. From the outset the choice was controversial, due to its proximity to the exposed north coast. Some said the station should have been located nearer the centre of horticultural production, between Hayle and Penzance. Others argued that it was a useful test-bed, because whatever could be achieved there should be repeatable almost anywhere in the West. With hindsight, there was some justification for either view. The site was far from ideal, too cool and exposed for many kinds of horticulture, but for shelter trials and work on daffodils and brassicas, it served its purpose well, and as the shelter trees and hedges grew, a wider range of crops prospered.

The subject of Rosewarne EHS and its satellite stations at Elbridge in the Tamar Val-

Fred Shepherd, Rosewarne's first Director, and 'Shepherd's Hey', named in his honour (above). An aerial view of Rosewarne, c. 1980, below. The Camborne by-pass bisected the site in 1973–4.

ley and St Mary's on the Isles of Scilly, would each fill a book. Not only would this record their achievements, but also it would relate how they impacted upon the careers and lives of so many horticulturists who worked

Rosewarne staged many shows in the UK and Holland. The photograph (1988) shows the author (left)
with Don Gilbert, National Bulbs Adviser, setting up a trade show exhibit at NEC, Birmingham.

at these centres over the years. In the early days, Rosewarne staff numbered over 100 as the station widened its interest into a host of flower, vegetable and fruit crops. Trials included crop nutrition, cultivations and bulky manures, the latter necessitating the gathering of seaweed and the keeping of cattle and pigs. Events, characters and stories, many amusing, now almost folklore, reflect the loyalty and cohesion found in this community of horticulturists. Each station developed close relationships with the horticultural areas it served, which tended to be compact and rather specialized. Perhaps this was eventually their undoing, for it was found, when the crunch came, that the financial support they could command was localized and therefore limited.

Fred Shepherd set out with high ambitions, and after a modest start, with the staff occupying two Nissen huts, the station began to take shape and the budget grew. Fred created a new layout of farm roads, and planted shelterbelts and hedges, confirming the value of combining Monterey Pine, Monterey Cypress and Escallonia 'Crimson Spire'. Glasshouses and other buildings followed, including a remarkable packing shed acquired, apparently, from the aircraft industry, and against whose south wall still thrive the much publicized Kiwi fruits. Much of the ambitious range of crops, including fruit trees and bushes, succumbed to the salty westerly gales, and were soon abandoned. Yet early photographs show the high standard of cultivation and experimentation despite the difficulties.

Daffodils occupied a key position from the beginning. Fred Shepherd was a daffodil enthusiast, and registered several varieties of daffodils personally as well as writing the RHS daffodil booklet. He gathered together some excellent people, many of whom remained loyal staff until the station's closure in 1989. Perhaps the most significant, as far as daffodils are concerned, was Barbara Fry, who joined the staff in 1958 (see also Chapter 3, 'Famous Cornish daffodil breeders') and, with considerable insight, was given responsibility for the daffodil variety trial. Fred Shepherd and Barbara Fry were co-authors of Rosewarne's first daffodil variety report in 1962, and there followed a series of 'Yellow Books' which listed in detail the yields and characteristics of over 2,000 daffodil varieties between 1955 and 1984.

The next phase was under the directorship of Jim Eaton. Jim had been County Horticultural Adviser in Worcestershire, and had a strong interest in work-study, which was fashionable at that time. His brief was to downsize the operation. Many of the plant collections were disposed of, and the emphasis changed to crop development and mechanization, two areas in which he excelled. Under his guidance, the machinery workshop team and others introduced improvements in bulb handling and cauliflower harvesting, and did pioneering work on the production and harvesting of 'St Piran' anemone corms, a strain raised by Betty Jeff and Margaret Gill.

At this time Bill Wallis was conducting trials which were laying the foundations for a modern bulb industry. Taking over from Bill in 1969, the author was not alone in admiring his predecessor's detailed experimental approach. The 1968 Rosewarne Report contained the results of pre-cooling trials on 'Golden Harvest' and 'Magnificence'. Bulbs

'Eaton Song', a sister of 'Cornish Chuckles', is named after Jim Eaton, Rosewarne's second Director.

received different periods of cooling over different dates. Grower Charles Le Grice referred to the 1968 Report as his 'Bible'. Rosewarne's reports and papers delivered at National Conferences and International Bulb Symposia flowed in an increasing stream from the early days right up to closure in 1989.

Jim Eaton made a significant decision when he invited Barbara Fry to start breeding daffodils. This was something of a departure for an experimental station, since some held that plant breeding was the province of the geneticist. However, in justifying this step, Rosewarne was already engaged in two crop improvement programmes: one for winter cauliflower (broccoli in Cornwall), and the other for anemones. Jim persuaded HQ in London that a daffodil programme should be added.

The key to achieving early flowering was the variety 'Rijnveld's Early Sensation', a flower of modest quality and short stem. The quest for extreme earliness had seldom been a major objective of daffodil breeders. Daffodil shows tend to be later than the main commercial season, and for most breeders there is more to be gained from seeking novelty and perfection of form.

In Cornwall, 'Rijnveld's Early Sensation' (above left) blooms before Christmas. It formed the basis of Rosewarne's breeding programme.
One Cornish farm sold a million bunches of 'Barenwyn' (above right) before 19 January in 2001. 'Tamara' (left) is not a high-quality flower, but it is early and highly productive.

'Rijnveld's Early Sensation' (RES) is, as its name implies, a sensational variety, but its parentage is unknown. It was raised by F. Herbert Chapman of Rye, Sussex, who began raising daffodils in 1904; but it was named and registered by F. Rijnveld & Sons in Holland in 1956, 11 years after Chapman's death. If called simply 'Early Sensation', there is a risk of confusion since there is another daffodil with this name, of Dutch origin, but with none of the amazing earliness of 'Rijnveld's'. RES has a short cold requirement, which means that it can grow before the winter has really begun.

'Dan du Plessis' (left) and 'Mike Pollock' (right) are two new 'Matador' × jonquilla hybrids named by Cornish growers in 1996.

In the past it usually flowered at about Christmas or New Year, but it has bloomed considerably earlier than this in recent years. Jim Eaton reasoned that hybridizing could bridge the six weeks' difference between RES and most other early varieties. Consequently, one of the first successes was by crossing it with 'Trenance', an early yellow daffodil raised by Dr Favell. A selection from this pairing is 'Tamara', one of the best known of the new generation of January daffodils.

A string of new early varieties followed, which have given a new lease of life to the Cornish industry and underpin the increasing confidence of growers in recent years.

Barbara Fry went on to create more diverse hybrids, using other parents, which she selected with great care. 'St Keverne' was a favourite

flower and when, among its numerous good qualities, it proved to have basal rot resistance, it was frequently used as both male and female parent. Many of the new stocks show disease resistance and are now widely grown, despite the fact that 'St Keverne' itself has fallen out of favour. Names like 'Tamsyn', 'Armynel' ('King Midas'), 'Golden Anniversary', 'Trelawney Gold', 'Dellan' and others could be important for years to come. One farm recently reported that 'Barenwyn', an early trumpet daffodil released in 1985, yielded a million bunches, mostly for export, before 19 January.

In 1968, Rosewarne EHS turned its attention to the tazetta group of narcissi, the principal crop of the Isles of Scilly. Using the very early flowering New Zealand variety 'Autumn Sol' a breakthrough was possible, with

'January Gold', originally named 'First Hope' (left) is an early, free-flowering choice for the garden. 'Cornish Chuckles' (right) could replace 'Tête à Tête' as the top garden variety.

'Innisidgen' now opening the Isles of Scilly season in September.

Fellow breeders like to exchange information and material, and Barbara Fry corresponded with many people including Harry Tuggle Jr. of Maryland, USA. He brought to her notice the potential of 'Matador', a big, boldly coloured, fertile tazetta. When Harry died in 1969, quantities of his stocks and seeds were despatched to Rosewarne by his executors. Hybrids, which he never saw bloom, turned out to be exceptionally strong and colourful varieties covering a long season. Being winter-growing tazettas, most were considered best suited to Scillonian conditions, and as 'Hugh Town', 'Scilly Valentine' and 'Royal Connection', they are widely grown. Others with jonquil characteristics,

such as 'Martinette', 'Dan du Plessis' and 'Mike Pollock' remained in Cornwall. Rosewarne also bred some very good double daffodils, and until its closure continued to hybridize daffodils under a contract with local growers.

Along the way, a number of dwarf varieties were produced, which were better suited to garden or pot culture. The UK industry has tended to be reluctant to develop small daffodils. 'Small Fry' and 'Bob Minor', intended to be a lasting tribute to Barbara's work, have disappeared, along with 'Gold Top', once said to be the best ever pot daffodil. 'January Gold', originally registered as 'First Hope', survives and should be more widely grown because it is very early and prolific. Daffodil pedants tend to disapprove of its tendency to produce seven- or eight-petalled flowers instead of

Mike Pollock (left) and Jim Hosking were the final Director and Chairman of Rosewarne EHS.

the usual six; but this is surely excusable in a January flower! One dwarf variety for which there are high hopes is 'Cornish Chuckles'.

The task of marketing the Rosewarne daffodil seedlings fell to the Station's third Director, Mike Pollock, who did a very good job within the rules imposed by the government for the marketing of government-raised material. These stated that the whole of a bulb stock must go to the highest bidder. This led to the formation of the Cornwall Area Bulb Growers' Association (CABGA), which proved a shrewd move, enabling Cornish growers to make a corporate bid. There were occasions when 'eggs in several baskets' would have been safer.

When Rosewarne closed in 1989, the greenhouses and other facilities soon became neglected and wind-torn. Rumours abounded

that the site might be developed as a County Council depot or a riding centre. After three years, and assisted by the European LEADER Project, the County Council became owners and leased it to the Duchy College as a horticultural centre for education and training. For the staff and growers who had been involved with the station this was one of the best of the possible outcomes.

Still, many years after its closure there remains great pride in Rosewarne, the standards it maintained, and what it achieved. The author recalls Station Chairman and grower Mr Robert Meneer addressing staff prior to a visit by HQ personnel: 'Don't worry, be confident. You can do things here that cannot be done elsewhere in Britain.' It was not unusual, after such occasions, to be told, 'We did not realize you were doing such interesting work!'

Rosewarne always gave of its best, and its work was respected both at home and abroad. One legacy of Rosewarne's early days, the Sou'westers Horticultural Club, founded by Fred Shepherd, continues to flourish with a new generation of young growers swelling its membership.

Ellbridge Experimental Station was near Plymouth, and served the mixed horticultural cropping of the Tamar Valley, which was important for early strawberries, protected crops and flowers, while Trenoweth, on the Isles of Scilly, was established primarily to help the growers of 'Soleil d'Or' narcissi. Rosewarne and the two satellites replaced former stations run by the County Council at Gulval, near Penzance, Bere Alston, on the Devon side of the Tamar, and Holy Vale on St Mary's.

The five-acre unit at Ellbridge was established in 1929, and became attached to Rosewarne in 1954. Until its closure in 1977, it was considered an ideal model for development and advisory work, with information being created and applied locally. Its south-facing slopes could be relied upon to provide a useful population of Narcissus Fly. Entomologists from Starcross Laboratories showed how very effective aldrin was, reducing a 55 per cent attack to almost nil. Work was also carried out to demonstrate safe hot-water treatment of the temperamental narcissus 'Tamar Valley Double White'. Ellbridge proved an excellent training ground for Ministry horticultural advisers, several of whom moved on to high office. The centre closed after 50 years supporting businesses in East Cornwall and West Devon, and the work on strawberries and narcissi found application beyond the South West.

The Isles of Scilly sub-station, Trenoweth, St Mary's, was set up in 1967, and the Royal connection was established right from the start with a visit by four members of the Royal Family. For several years the centre was managed by Neville Goodway, the local adviser, but in 1973 he was moved to the mainland, and it became fully attached to Rosewarne. In that same year, a joint annual report described two very significant developments: the introduction and testing of virus-free 'Soleil d'Or', and the use of polythene covers to advance flowering. The new stock reversed the decline in 'Soleil d'Or', and the *in situ* treatments replaced the former methods for producing early crops. The story of this specialized industry is recounted in Chapter 6, 'Scilly: the fortunate isles' and 'A burning question'.

In 1992, three years after the closure of its parent station, Trenoweth passed into the control of a board of growers, and the centre continues under local management with technical advice from the author. It is currently funded by UK/EU grants, members' subscriptions, the Duchy of Cornwall, the Island Council, and some contract work.

The rise and fall of 'St Keverne'

Among the important varieties raised by P.D. Williams and his son Michael, two stand out: 'Carlton' and 'Saint Keverne', which are both yellow, large-cupped (Division 2) daffodils. 'Carlton' was named before 1927, preceding the other by some 30 years.

'Carlton' was never as popular as 'King Alfred' or 'Golden Harvest' in Cornwall, because it flowers in March, and in the Scillies it is prone to *Botrytis* 'spot'. However, in Lincolnshire and Holland it dominated, with an estimated 30 per cent of production at its peak in the 1970s.

Michael Williams registered 'St Keverne' in 1934, a year before his father's death. It is a

Confirming that 'St Keverne' is resistant to basal rot gave new impetus to breeding and research. Unfortunately, its downfall is a susceptibility to virus.

fine, quality flower, which still wins prizes at shows, some 70 years later. It has very respectable parents, stated to be 'Royalist' and 'King Alfred'. Many writers have extolled the qualities of 'St Keverne', and when its resistance to basal rot was confirmed, growers backed it heavily, causing the bulbs to be in great demand, and expensive.

Unfortunately, at a time when 'St Keverne' was enjoying its greatest popularity, virus symptoms became an increasing problem, resulting in it failing growing season inspections, which were necessary for an export permit, and it had to be admitted that the variety was no longer suitable for large-scale production. This was a huge disappointment within the industry, not least for those growers who had invested heavily in it.

Possible solutions to the problem were examined, first to create virus-free stock, as was done a few years earlier with 'Soleil d'Or', or to concentrate on the new varieties raised from 'St Keverne'. Both options were followed, but have taken time to evaluate. Virus-free bulbs of 'St Keverne' were produced but are now, some 20 years later, again becoming infected. As far as 'St Keverne' seedlings like 'Tamsyn', 'Dellan', 'King Midas', 'Emblyn' and 'Golden Anniversary' are concerned, these are excellent varieties, but as regards their long-term future, the jury will remain out for some time yet. Where good stock can be found, 'St Keverne' is still a superb variety, durable and wind resistant in the garden. As a cut flower, its smallish brown bud is now seen as a disadvantage, hastening its decline.

Meanwhile, 'Carlton', the older of the two Williams varieties, has proved highly durable in commerce, and remains generally unaffected by viruses.

A nice warm bath

The process of soaking bulbs for several hours in a tank of warm water sounds unsophisticated and laborious for a modern industry. It seems incredible that this technique, devised in 1917 to control eelworms, has remained essentially unchanged. Nevertheless, daffodil growers throughout the world use hot-water treatment (HWT) to maintain healthy stocks, and to date no reliable alternative has been found. The treatment is used before planting commercial crops; it is not applied to bulbs for immediate sale.

By planting 'sterilized' bulbs, the grower expects them to remain pest free for several years at the very least, and regards treatment as a form of insurance. Dry heat, chemical dips, gasses and 'high-tech' ideas such as X-rays and microwaves have all been tried, but none are effective or achieve the critical distinction between killing the pest and killing the bulb. In the 1960s, the organophosphate chemical Nemaphos was introduced by Cyanamid and used by some growers. Its toxicity necessitated full protective clothing for the operator, and many growers would not use it, especially if they already had hot-water equipment, so there were few regrets when the product was withdrawn, primarily because it gave unpredictable results. The reason for this is of some interest. Nemaphos often failed when eelworms had already caused severe rotting of the bulb. Whereas heat penetrates a bulb by conduction, a systemic chemical only enters living bulb tissue. Hence, it does not reach an adequate concentration in the decayed parts where eelworms are most numerous.

As we saw in Chapter 4, 'Trials and Tribulations', in addition to killing eelworm, HWT kills Narcissus Fly and Bulb Scale Mite, and can reduce the incidence of some diseases.

When James Ramsbottom, working at Wisley, presented the results of his trials in 1917, he proposed a four-hour soak at 43.3° C (110° F). This information came just in time to save the industry from collapse. Later, the soaking time was modified to three hours at 44.4° C (112° F), and this remains the basic recommendation today, although further fine-tuning has occurred over the years.

The discovery of HWT was such a relief to a desperate and grateful industry that, for a time, its limitations were accepted. However, it became evident that sometimes the flowers

In the early days, metal cages were filled with crates of bulbs and raised and lowered by overhead hoist within a building. Today, most treatment tanks are in the open.

and bulbs were damaged, and the pest was not always totally eradicated.

In the 1940s, while studying air temperatures at Kirton Experimental Station, James Wood made a very important finding. He showed that the severity of HWT damage to the bulb and the bud inside depended upon the storage temperature prior to treatment. By keeping the bulbs warm for a while before dipping, the risks were much reduced. This proved to be hugely significant in Cornwall, where flowers were such a priority, and today bulbs are stored at 30° C for one week before HWT, so that they produce good growth and marketable 'first year' flowers.

As for the occasions when the eelworms were not all killed, since even a few survivors can soon lead to another outbreak, more research was needed. Nematologists have long known that stem and bulb eelworms have extraordinary powers of survival: under dry conditions, the microscopic 'pre-adult' eelworms cluster together to form 'eelworm wool', which can remain viable for years and resist HWT. Unfortunately, this greatly complicates the whole question of 'pre-warming' the bulbs to prevent damage to the embryo flower, since warming induces resistance in the nematodes. This posed a real problem.

Growers are divided between those who want to sell good quality 'first-year' flowers, and those primarily interested in bulb production, who do not mind if the flowers are damaged. The former store bulbs at 30° C, then soak them and apply HWT at 46.7° C (116° F) for three hours. The latter hold them at 18° C, and treat at 44.4° C (112° F). The addition of formaldehyde and a wetter (detergent) to the soaks improves results and kills fungal spores.

Although HWT has remained essentially the same for 80 years, the equipment used and the

The flowers on the left (var. 'Ellen') show typical hot-water damage. The others were pre-warmed before treatment. The discovery of pre-warming was a major advance.

bulb handling systems have changed beyond recognition. The earliest dipping tanks were simple affairs, with bulbs contained in nets or wire crates, lowered in and out of the water manually. Heating systems were also primitive: perhaps a paraffin burner turned up or down according to a thermometer in the water. Improvements were added later, such as thermostatic control, a circulating pump, and a hoist to raise or lower the load – a process known as 'dunking'. Some new systems employ a 'drive in' method, whereby the empty tank is loaded sideways by forklift truck. Once loaded, the door is shut and the hot water pumped in from a 'slave' tank.

A major advance in the 1970s was the use of large wooden boxes, or bulk bins, holding

Hot-water treatment is carried out in a clean area away from possible sources of re-infection. Dipping tanks are mechanically loaded (above and below left). The water contains wetter — detergent — and dilute formaldehyde to kill spores and dried eelworms. Hot-wateer tanks require occasional topping up (below right), followed by a temperature boost.

An alternative to the dunking system is the front-loading tank (above). Modern tanks have powerful water circulation pumps to ensure a uniform temperature throughout. With front-loading tanks, the pumps also need to empty and refill quickly. Below: Loading a bulb store calls for careful planning to ensure that the loads can be taken out in proper sequence.

up to one tonne of bulbs, which could be used for both storing and dipping. Initially some growers were sceptical, voicing fears that bulbs would be damaged or would simply rot, but these fears proved unfounded, and now all major growers use bins for drying, storing, dipping and tipping into the planting machine. The key to successful 'bulk handling' is to keep air circulating through the bins at all times by the use of fans.

Pre-cooling bulbs for early flowering

Spring-flowering bulbs need a period of cold before they respond to the rising temperatures.

Information about pre-cooling bulbs (often referred to as 'preparing') came from Holland. It was first used as a means of producing earlier forced flowers, but before long it

A store can cool bulbs or flowers, according to season. Like many Scillonians, Francis Hicks of St Agnes is a keen bird watcher, and always carries binoculars.

was shown that the same treatment (six weeks at 9° C (48° F) would advance outdoor crops in the milder counties. The technique presented a problem for the open-ground grower, since pre-cooling bulbs without first applying HWT might invite an eelworm outbreak, but if HWT damaged the flowers, there would be little point in using the advancing treatment. This was why pre-warming before HWT was such an important development for the West Country grower. Timing HWT is also important in producing good first-year growth and flowering. During the summer, in the bulb's centre, miniature petals, anthers and pistil appear in sequence until finally, in late July, the cup or trumpet (paracorolla) emerges, looking like a 'mini-skirt' between the line of the petals and the anthers. Known as the Pc stage, this is the preferred time to apply HWT, which can be followed by cool storage.

Going bananas!

When daffodil stems are laid flat, they begin to bend under the influence of gravity. This has proved a problem since bunches are mostly packed flat in boxes for market, and after a day or so can give the impression that they are drying up like a slice of bread left on a plate. The bending, to produce what have been called 'banana bunches', is the plant's attempt to straighten up.

Left: The 'banana' phenomenon is greatest with tight-picked buds. The bunches on the left are also shorter than the more developed ones. Rosewarne compared upright packing with the traditional flat cardboard box (below). The recently developed plastic box packed upright (above right) avoids the problem of stem-bending.

Unfortunately, as the picking stage of daffodils has become earlier, the tendency to form 'bananas' increases. With more developed flowers the bending is slower, and more confined to the stem bases.

There are two means of reducing the problem. Growers normally put buds straight into cold store after picking to keep them fresh and prevent them 'popping' open. Storage at about 1° C also slows down the rate of stem bending, but does not entirely prevent it. A more positive means of avoiding it is to keep stems upright, both in store and on the journey to market, and today many growers use a returnable plastic box known as a 'Procona', in which bunches are tightly packed together. These boxes are stackable, and the flowers can be given water, but it has to be said that such returnable boxes are not as popular as the standard flat cardboard cartons. The upright market pack bears a resemblance to the hatbox used by Scillonian farmer William Trevellick in about 1870. Perhaps William knew a thing or two!

6

Scilly, Tamar and Lincolnshire

Scilly: the fortunate isles

In their book *The Fortunate Isles*, Ernest and Rex Bowley took their title from the Greek mythological name for the Isles of Scilly, The Hesperides – meaning Isles of the Blest, Elysian Fields, Atlantis, or Fortunate Isles, where the inhabitants dwelt in sunny, flower-filled meadows, and dead heroes could be laid to rest in perpetual summer and peace. Most people would agree that the Islands are magical, but until the advent of narcissus growing and, more recently, tourism, they were, at times, a place of great poverty and hardship, far removed from the image created in classical times.

The Islands hold a unique place in the cultivation of narcissi – a fact recognized by MAFF in 1967, when it set up a centre on St Mary's to study the crop. Long before this, narcissi had transformed the livelihood of the island population, and subsequently the demands and practices of growing the crop have become embedded in the culture and reflected in the landscape of these small, sheltered fields.

There was a time when the Islanders produced a wide range of crops on their farms. Potatoes and vegetables were produced for an early harvest, or because St Mary's was a final opportunity for transatlantic shipping to pick up fresh supplies. Several factors have contributed to the disappearance of most crops other than narcissi, the major reason being overwhelming competition from lower cost producers elsewhere. Despite their enviable climate, the Scillies impose several limitations for growers. The pattern of small farms, salty winds and a limited water supply, coupled with a gritty soil and frequent summer drought, creates problems. In addition to this, there are the costs and problems associated with shipping produce to markets. Fortunately, tazetta narcissi thrive under these conditions, and coexist happily with the display of summer wild flowers and wildlife so attractive to visitors. Countryside Stewardship Schemes, supported by most tenant farmers and the Wildlife Trust, and the Islands' status as an area of

The flowers of tazetta narcissi are marketed slightly open to reveal their colour and scent.

Taking flowers by donkey cart on the Islands (above). Loading the ship for the mainland (below), c. *1910.*

A gig used for inter-island transport (above). Loading the launch Lyonesse *on St Agnes (below),* c. *1910.*

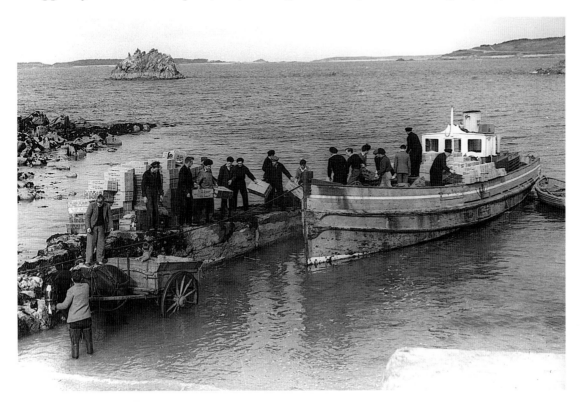

Small, sheltered fields are typical of the Islands, and provide essential protection for the crop (above).
Pittosporum crassifolium *(below) is the preferred hedging shrub.*

outstanding natural beauty (AONB), together with the Duchy of Cornwall's influence, all help to maintain the beauty and diversity of the landscape.

The Isles of Scilly daffodil show in March 1886 was the first of its kind anywhere in the country. It did not go unnoticed by the *Gardeners' Chronicle* magazine which, in announcing the show, wrote:

> it speaks of difficulties overcome, it speaks of new prosperity for the Islanders, of the banishment of famine, of the establishment of industry and of the promotion of happiness

This show was almost 40 years before the first Western Commercial Spring Show in

A tall screen of elms protects this field of jonquils (above). So far, the Islands have escaped the ravages of Dutch Elm disease. 'Soleil d'Or' (below) is the principal variety on the Islands.

Penzance in 1924, and the Tamar Valley Spring Show in 1925. Records of the early shows are hazy, and the two world wars interrupted the sequence, but in 1949 there were three shows on the Islands: one for early narcissi in January; the main show in early March, and another on 12 November. Noteworthy is the fact that at the November show there were 'Soleil d'Or', 'Paper White' and 'Gloriosus' narcissi alongside the chrysanthemums. Clearly, the production of early narcissi was well established.

Transport and marketing have always been major challenges. With storms at sea, and fog closing in over the Islands and Land's End, the best laid marketing plans can be subject to delays. Formerly, individual growers despatched flowers to their own selection of provincial market salesmen throughout the country.

*'Scent from the Islands' (above) is a successful postal flower business based on St Martin's.
While men brave the elements, women 'tie' and pack the flowers indoors (above and below, respectively).*

Co-operation in marketing did not always succeed, but in the early twenty-first century, Mainland Marketing, managed by Andrew May and Keith Hale, has set standards of flower quality and presentation that enable the product to be despatched to any buyer in the UK or abroad. A recent and highly successful venture has been 'Scent from the Islands', a postal service based on St Martin's, developed by Andrew and Hilary Julian, which concentrates on show pinks in summer and narcissi in winter and spring.

Many farms, with assistance from European and national funding, have modernized their buildings, facilities and equipment. The number of fully commercial producers continues to decline, which does give those remaining the possibility of acquiring more land and

A gas-burning machine destroys old crop debris, and improves the next season's crop.

resting some of it from narcissus by growing a 'break' crop. Since the cessation of potato growing, there has been less incentive to gather seaweed as a manure, and there is concern that the land is becoming impoverished, as evidenced by cases of boron deficiency in recent years. There are plans to increase the numbers of livestock, and with them more grass and fodder crops to improve soil fertility. Local meat and other products offered to visitors will enhance, however briefly, their experience of life on the 'Fortunate Isles'.

A burning question

The mild winters, warm, rather dry summers and sandy soils of the Scillies suit the cultivation of the tazetta group of narcissi (Division 8). The climate is the nearest of anywhere in the UK to that of the Mediterranean, and even mainland West Cornwall is not quite as favour-able for these heat-loving bulbs. Since tazettas have grown on the Islands since the Middle Ages, it is very likely that William Trevellick's famous hatbox of 130 years ago contained 'Scilly White', 'Primo' and 'Soleil d'Or' – bulb stocks which are still with us today.

For many years, growers on the Scillies have burnt straw to clean the bulb fields in summer, and it was noticed that tazetta narcissi flowered earlier after such treatment. The explanation for this phenomenon remained hidden for years, although numerous theories were proposed. One suggestion was that heat from the burning straw drew up moisture from below, but this was discounted when trials showed that watering did not evoke the response. Neither did the potash-rich ash from burnt straw reproduce the effect. The practice did result in a slight rise in soil temperature, but at bulb depth this was negligible and short-

Early summer polythene coverage of tazetta beds advances flowering. Applied in late summer and autumn it retards growth.

lived, and again, unlikely to account for the improved growth.

During the 1970s, Rosewarne obtained similar results from burning-over 'Wedgwood' iris, and this attracted the interest of Dutch research workers because iris had always been an important crop in Holland. One trial on the Isles of Scilly seemed to offer an explanation. It was after the drought year of 1976, when imported straw became very expensive, that propane gas burners were used on the 'Soleil d'Or' beds. By flaming the dead leaf and weed residue several times instead of just once, the effect on the bulbs was magnified, suggesting that each pass of the burner added a 'dose' of *something*. Dutch and Japanese researchers subsequently confirmed that the active agent was smoke, containing the very versatile plant hormone ethylene.

Since this discovery, 'Soleil d'Or' growers, in addition to burning over, also cover plots with plastic sheeting and pump smoke beneath it. The combination of heat and smoke produces the pre-Christmas crop. This technique replaced the laborious and unreliable former method of producing early flowers by bulb storage. The *in situ* treatment can be applied to established beds to produce high yields and good quality flowers. It is significant that burning over or smoking is of no value on large-flowered daffodils. These northern species have never needed to adapt to fire. Instead, they have a cold requirement, which prevents autumn growth, safeguarding them from the damaging effects of winter frosts. On the Scillies, clear polythene coverage in late summer and autumn is also used to retard growth and flowering.

The Tamar Valley and the 'Double White'

The meandering River Tamar, which carves out the boundary between Devon and Cornwall, created an area which has been an important horticultural district for almost 200 years. Its steep slopes of differing aspect present a variety of microclimates, some south-facing, warm and sunny, others cool and moist, and the valley is spared the stinging, salt-laden gales suffered by growers further west. Early fruit, vegetables and flowers on these quiet hillsides were initially aimed at the Plymouth market, and were shipped to the city down river. In those pioneering days, the necessity to employ hand labour to work the steep slopes was no great cause for complaint, since physical work was the norm. Neither was it an insurmountable problem to convey soil that constantly eroded off the slopes back to the top of the field, since many of the men who took to the land had mining in their blood and understood how to haul soil or plough the land using pulleys.

Daffodil growing began in this area about 1905, but the more important enterprise, dating from the middle of the nineteenth century, was strawberries, following completion of the railway between Plymouth and London in 1849. The warm slopes and friable soil suited early strawberries, and it was thought that the twice-daily rise and fall of the tide moved the air and reduced the risk of frost.

The first narcissi to be grown were 'Van Sion', 'Maximus', 'Golden Spur', some tazettas – doubtless from the Isles of Scilly – and poets, including 'Double White'. Not surprisingly, the tazettas failed to thrive in the valley, and ominously there were reports that eelworm was making its presence felt, the steep slopes serving to spread the pest with the eroding soil.

'Tamar Valley Double White' was the valley's speciality. A lovely May flower, but not the easiest of daffodils to grow successfully.

One of the first daffodil growers was Mr J.P. Cloake of Cargreen. He kept a record of market returns for the ten years up to 1915, confirming the importance of 'Tamar Valley Double White', which returned 10–14 shillings per dozen bunches – double what was received for others such as 'Golden Spur', 'Primo' and 'Ornatus'. Daffodil crops often occupied the land beneath fruit trees, including cherries, for which the valley was famous.

At the start of the twenty-first century, with the exception of some excellent specialized glasshouse nurseries on the flatter land, there is little commercial horticulture carried on in the valleys. Much of the land has returned 'full circle' to the scrub and woodland from which it was reclaimed long ago.

The steep banks of the Tamar Valley (above) were important for early crops, but increasing costs have seen the land return 'full circle' to scrub and woodland. Conditions there were suited to growing 'Double Whites' and 'Poets', which have 'necky' bulbs (below left) compared with the rounded tazetta bulb (below right).

At the height of daffodil growing in the Tamar Valley, 'Double White' was the star performer. There has been much debate as to its origins, but the Tamar Valley always claimed to possess the true double 'gardenia-scented' form. Today, this lovely flower is seldom grown, partly because it is very late flowering, but also because it is not the easiest variety to grow well. If the weather prior to flowering in May is dry, the flower bud may shrivel and die. This is a problem shared with other double daffodils. 'Double White' is also an expensive bulb to handle, being elongated and 'necky', and the bulbs prefer to be left undisturbed, a

Women and girls packing flowers in the Tamar Valley in the 1940s (above). Note the bunching frames and neat raffia ties. Soil erosion was a major problem on the steep slopes, and a converted car chassis, called an 'earthcar' (below), could be used to haul the soil back up to the top.

factor which can encourage eelworm attack. Hot-water treating 'Double Whites' requires extra care to avoid damaging the bulb's roots which reappear early, even in store, despite the lateness of this variety. 'Double Whites' succeeded better in the balmy atmosphere of the Tamar than almost anywhere else, and benefited from river dredgings of mud and fallen leaves applied to the land. A collection of daffodils, including many of the older ones at the National Trust Gardens at Cotehele, on the bank of the Tamar, is reawakening an interest in this traditional crop of the Tamar Valley.

In Lincolnshire, bulbs are forced on a large scale under glass (above). Forced daffodils are cut with the enclosing basal sheath (below). The loss of the leaf usually renders the bulbs useless.

The Lincolnshire connection

The flower bulb industry in Lincolnshire began in much the same way and at a similar time as that of the Isles of Scilly. Prior to 1880, flowers were grown on vegetable market gardens on the outskirts of cities, but new and more specialized areas of production developed, and these sent their produce further afield. Early records tell of consignments of bulb flowers sent from the Spalding area to city markets in orange boxes and apple hampers.

The deep silt soils of Lincolnshire's flat land proved excellent for bulb growing, and in the early twentieth century many different kinds were grown. Tulips and daffodils predominated, all being spaced by hand in plough furrows, creating beautifully arranged beds stretching to the horizon. Many Dutchmen established businesses in the Eastern counties, finding conditions not unlike those of Holland.

After forcing, the boxes are stacked, and the bulbs are usually destroyed.

As the UK bulb acreage grew, reaching a peak of 3,000 hectares in 1939, mechanization increased, and the priority in Lincolnshire was to produce bulbs for forcing under glass in winter.

From Victorian times, before large-scale commercial flower production had begun, gardeners in private gardens and estates were knowledgeable in the art of forcing bulbs. The trick, as with strawberries, was to leave the plants outside to experience enough cold weather before bringing them into the warmth; an insufficient period outside resulted in slow and feeble growth. However, knowing just how much cold was enough was always the problem. The safest policy was to wait until the tip of the bud could be seen in the neck of the bulb.

Open-ground daffodils in Cornwall and the Isles of Scilly could always gain a four- to five-week advantage over those of the colder, eastern counties. As production increased and bulbs became cheaper, the 'up-country' forcing industry developed and, despite its higher costs, it had the advantages of a more controlled output and proximity to the markets. By the middle of the twentieth century, glasshouse forcing was carried on throughout the UK. Forced daffodils cropped with leaves attached are so weakened that they are usually dumped afterwards, but at times of high bulb prices they can be 'reclaimed' by replanting them in open ground for two years. Meanwhile, many Cornish growers preferred to plant 'prepared' bulbs in open ground and, since only the stems are picked, the bulbs remained *in situ* for the next year.

Over the years, heating and labour costs have risen considerably, threatening the forcing industry, but it still survives, mainly because growers use bulbs produced on their own farm, coupled with revolutionary mechanization and production techniques. In place of straw-covered 'standing grounds' where boxed bulbs were rooted, today's forcers convey a succession of pallet-loads by fork-lift truck from cold store to glasshouse, and the precise cold requirement is given to each batch to allow a rapid turn-round of crops.

Since the mid-1960s, the opportunity for early, low-cost daffodil production in Cornwall has tempted some large 'up-country' businesses to establish farms in the county. Several of these have been highly successful and remain major enterprises today. However, there have been occasional miscalculations – for instance, when large fields were created for bulb growing near Land's End, only to find that salt-laden winds proved very damaging to the crop. In such matters there is no substitute for local knowledge.

7

What of the Future?

Whither the trade shows?

In the first half of the twentieth century, daffodil growers enjoyed showing and competing. There was the pride of winning and receiving trophies, while also showing off their latest achievements to the public and the trade. Spring shows were a landmark in the growers' calendar – a shop window and an occasion to increase business.

The first daffodil show was held on St Mary's, in the Isles of Scilly, in 1886. This was followed by Truro in 1897, where the exhibitors were cousins J.C. and P.D. Williams, Barr's of Covent Garden, Ware's of Tooting, and other industry leaders. The Cornwall Daffodil and Spring Flower Society held shows until the Cornwall Garden Society took over in 1957.

Penzance Spring Show, in mid-March, was one of the first flower shows of the year, and announced that, at last, 'hesitant spring' might perhaps give way to consistently better days. For many years local growers competed in strongly contested commercial classes, but interest has waned as a different marketing pattern has evolved. Gradually, regional and provincial wholesalers withdrew their support, and as the market pack changed from open bloom to green buds, the colour and most of the skill in bunching and packing has been lost. Production units are now huge businesses, and buyers for supermarkets and exporters are more remote than formerly.

The 1938 Penzance Spring Show Schedule listed classes for market packs of broccoli, spring cabbage and lettuce, and a range of flowers including violets, polyanthus and wallflowers. Additionally, each day between 5.30 p.m. and 7.00 p.m. competitions were held in which contestants prepared, bunched and packed flowers under the watchful gaze of the judges. Points were awarded 'for rapidity and the best finish'. There were sections for employers, employees and 'under 21s'. One wonders how many present-day employers or

On the Isles of Scilly, surplus flowers of highly perfumed varieties are being used for scent production by Peter Hobson at the Isles of Scilly Perfumery.

Exhibition flower packs and broccoli (winter cauliflower) at the Penzance Spring Show (above), 2004.
The daffodil show is an opportunity for breeders to present their latest achievements (below).

their staff would submit to such an examination! Like many other once-important rural activities, flower shows have changed greatly. They are still an enjoyable venue for competition, but increasingly provide a congenial setting for meeting friends, discussing horticulture, and admiring and purchasing plants, with photographic classes and children's collages introduced to fill the space.

Among the specialist daffodil breeders and exhibitors, interest in shows is still very strong, and the public enjoy the occasion. The season starts with the RHS Early Daffodil Show in Westminster in early March and, throughout the country, there are over 150 shows affiliated to the Daffodil Society, with the finale, in the North, in early May.

Francis Hosken, daffodil grower on St Mary's, Isles of Scilly, carries off several trophies.

Where do all the flowers go?

The UK produces more daffodils than any other flower, and also more than any other country. Cornwall's share of the national crop is increasing year by year and, in the early twenty-first century, is approaching 40 per cent. In 2003, a 200-hectare Cornish daffodil farm sold 6 million bunches (60 million stems), requiring a picking gang of 300. At a piecework rate of 6p per bunch, this puts the cost of picking alone on this farm at £360,000. Paying the wages on a daily basis is a major task, but one which is being eased by the increasing employment of foreign workers on a longer-term basis.

The overall output of the county is very difficult to estimate, because several factors make it uncertain how many flowers will actually be sold. Weather conditions, availability of pickers, and market demand all interact, sometimes resulting in considerable wastage. However, in an average year, Cornwall will produce a bunch of flowers and one or two bulbs per person in the UK.

Considerable quantities of both flowers and bulbs are exported – the main markets being Holland, Germany and the USA. These buyers have a strong preference for yellow trumpet daffodils, and although this also applies in the UK, the home market is, at last, becoming more interested in other colours, double flowers and the scented, multi-headed varieties.

Supermarkets at home and abroad are the main outlets, but during the daffodil season there emerge a vast number of sales points in both town and country, including greengrocers, garage forecourts and roadside stalls. Daffodils

A street flower stall sells many daffodils (above). No other flower is so readily available and cheerful, yet so modestly priced. Millions of daffodils beautify Britain's roadsides and by-passes each spring (below).

Daffodils accompany a happy wedding scene (above left). Growers are fortunate that Mothering Sunday falls in the flowering season (above right). Daffodils brighten an office (below).

are by far the cheapest flower available. Offering them in bud adds to the convenience of handling them, and to their enjoyment as they open. The recent development of a sleeve-pack gives the buds more protection, and an opportunity to brand the product and illustrate and name the flower.

Daffodil growers are fortunate that Valentine's Day, Mothering Sunday and Easter all fall within the flowering season, along with St David's Day in Wales, and St Piran's Day in Cornwall. A semi-serious attempt to move Mothering Sunday to a date in September received the support of chrysanthemum growers, but was rejected. Any change would risk losing the magic that daffodils bring to these spring festivals. Daffodils are welcome in any home, shop, office, classroom, church or

A well-stocked bulb shop offers a wide choice of varieties at farm prices (above). Attractive, well-illustrated pre-packs help promote sales (below).

Potting up bulbs for winter flowering is an enjoyable autumn job.

studio. There is scarcely a garden, park, city centre, by-pass or roundabout that is not brightened with daffodils as year by year, and with minimal attention, they add a splash of colour and convey an optimistic message of approaching spring.

The future

It is almost mandatory that a book such as this provides a glimpse of what the future may hold for the industry, its growers and workforce. With so many changes in production, marketing and the intensity of competition faced by growers, it is difficult to see ahead clearly. It seems that the only safe prediction is that change will continue, and recent trends towards increased scale, specialization, mechanization and automation are likely to quicken.

Competition from overseas over the whole range of horticultural produce has been increasing dramatically, and much UK horticulture has already haemorrhaged away. More and more developing nations are seeking to increase their foreign exchange, and often have significant advantages such as climate, low labour costs, government support, and perhaps less regulation. Global transport costs, despite the fuel used, seem to present little obstacle to the current trend.

Let us, for a moment, pause to consider those horticultural crops for which the UK is especially suited, and which are still economic to grow. There do not appear to be as many as there were in the mid-twentieth century. Britain was then virtually self-sufficient in most horticultural crops in their season. Fruit crops have been the greatest losers, with UK apple production halving since the 1980s. Large volumes of cut flowers like carnations and roses are flown in from distant countries, and each year supermarket shelves show that ever more of our vegetables and salads are coming from exotic places throughout the year.

However, against this trend, we have seen our ornamental plant and nursery stock sector enjoying expansion and profits in line with the burgeoning interest in home gardening, supported by magazines, television, and the development of attractive garden centres. Following a period of decline, there is also a revival in the production of soft fruits such as strawberries and raspberries, where advanced methods of protected growing are paying off, despite nimby opposition to poly-tunnels in some parts of the country.

In the flower sector, there is no doubt that the sale of reasonably priced flowers in supermarkets has lifted the UK shopper – formerly rather shy of buying flowers – up the European

Only by pursuing economies of scale and active marketing can businesses remain viable (above).
Bunches travel on a conveyor to the sleeve-wrapping machine (below). Photos at Winchester Growers Ltd.

Above: Sleeve-wrapped bunches are assembled for despatch to supermarkets. This development maintains freshness, and enables the customer to identify the product. Below: Loading daffodils near Penzance.

league. Unfortunately, most of the increased trade is in imported flowers, but strenuous efforts are being made to reverse this trend, especially in respect of summer flowers.

As for daffodils, we may be permitted a more optimistic view, because we are confident that the UK, and especially Cornwall, has probably the best climate in the world for the crop. The hotter countries are unsuitable for daffodils, and therefore cannot compete, and neither can those with an extreme continental climate. However, these factors alone will not necessarily guarantee a good long-term future for the daffodil grower. There remains the need to maintain the popularity of daffodils by offering the public the types of daffodils they want, and novelties each year.

Daffodils are a crop requiring a long-term commitment from the farmer. Because of this

The 'Bulb Mania' festivals at the Eden Project, near St Austell, are creating enormous interest in bulb planting, helping to support the Cornish industry.

the acreage tends to remain fairly stable, which is a good thing. The cost of planting stock is well above that of almost any other crop, and specialized buildings and equipment are required, together with technical know-how. These factors deter short-term uptake, and few farmers without previous experience risk taking up daffodil growing.

But will the demand be maintained? When every garden, park, city centre, by-pass and freeway is planted with daffodils, how many more bulbs will the public need? Properly managed, daffodils are long-lived plants, and the smaller gardens of today do not lend themselves to the extensive plantings of the past. While British growers continue to grow mainly the large-flowered daffodils for the cut-flower trade, their Dutch counterparts have switched

to the dwarf and pot types in response to the changing pattern of demand. Has the UK grower been slow to react to this trend? How is it that the ubiquitous little daffodil, 'Tête à Tête', bred in Cornwall, is produced almost entirely in Holland?

As cut flowers, daffodils are universally popular in the UK, and no other flower is so readily available and cheerful, yet so moderately priced. However, there are concerns over vase life. Being adapted to life in the cold, daffodils do not last as well in today's centrally heated homes as most other flowers, many of which benefit considerably from the little sachet of flower food often provided, something which has never proved to be of any value to daffodils or narcissi. And sadly, because daffodils are cheap, they often receive

The industry should promote the magic and excitement of bulbs.

scant attention in shops, supermarkets and other retail outlets, being poorly displayed, deprived of water and looking sad, or even still left in their box curled and dried. This is a matter that the industry must address if it wishes to see sales maintained.

The markets since the 1970s have encouraged an ever-tighter picking stage. Some producers regret this, but the industry has been powerless to slow the trend towards the 'green pencil'. For decades daffodils were sent to market as open flowers, but homes were considerably cooler in those days. In the middle of the twentieth century, the accepted marketing stage was termed 'goose neck' – when the bud had turned downwards and showed some colour, and was guaranteed to open. In short, by adhering to the 'green pencil' stage, is the industry failing to exploit the potential to sell a wider range of coloured daffodils, including the whites, reds and pinks in all their diverse shapes and sizes? Would not a cold retail counter help to display and popularize the many varieties available?

A steady reduction in the range of agrochemicals for use on horticultural crops is causing concern.

Horticultural crops classed as 'minor uses' are said not to justify the cost of obtaining approval from the regulatory authorities. Rightly, legislation will impose increasing demands on all farmers and growers to show care for the environment, the public and employees, and to observe protocols proposed by buyers.

Growers of crops with a high labour demand for harvesting have been finding it increasingly difficult to obtain sufficient workers as our indigenous workforce seems increasingly to shun field work. However, in the early years of the twenty-first century, the widening of Europe has persuaded many Eastern European seasonal workers to come to Britain. Initially some 'gang masters' were accused of exploitation, but matters are becoming better regulated, and improved terms and accommodation are being offered to the many, mostly young, workers who are gathering our crops. The future of these arrangements may be subject to changes, but any curtailment of foreign labour would be very unwelcome to UK growers.

The economics of growing over many years confirms that costs rise steadily, but prices received by the grower do not keep pace, and margins decline. It seems that only by pursuing economies of scale can businesses stay viable. So the number of small and medium-sized businesses will continue to decline unless they can co-operate in production and marketing.

Since the 1980s, Cornish daffodil growers have benefited enormously from growing early varieties, most of which were raised at Rosewarne EHS. These have greatly increased the volume of flowers marketed in January and the first half of February. The industry needs to be aware that this extra early production could create a situation of oversupply just as bad as before, but a month earlier. A campaign to sell more bulbs of these early varieties in the retail market would help, as would better statistics of what is actually being produced.

A more remote worry is that, in some unforeseen way, climate change might occur, to the disadvantage of Cornwall and the British Isles. This may sound alarmist, but an opposing view to that of general global warming is that warmer summers may occur, but a northward movement of the Gulf Stream could leave the UK shivering in winter along with much of the European mainland. However, so far the milder winters in Cornwall and the Isles of Scilly are bringing daffodils into flower earlier compared with the Rosewarne records of the 1960s.

The different situation of the Isles of Scilly grower has been highlighted several times. The unpalatable fact is that the long-term future of the Scillonian industry looks much less secure. The Islands' small, tenanted farms are less able to reduce costs of production by expansion, and without extra land on which to rotate the crop, problems and costs increase faster than market returns. Island horticulture is at the crossroads. Can the Islands' narcissus farms be maintained by a combination of publicity, tourism, countryside grants and diversification into niche crops, or is the only viable alternative just one or two flower farms in total? Great efforts are being made by all concerned within the Scillonian industry, and it seems that the only viable policy will be to promote specialist products with higher value. Perhaps the recent venture into producing narcissus scent will provide another source of income. The Islands have no desire to become a museum or theme park, and the legacy of narcissus growing going back over so many years must be worth preserving.

On an optimistic note, it is clear that, thanks to the imagination of Tim Smit and his team, Cornwall is now a top world tourist destination. The Eden Project is giving huge support to Cornish producers and businesses, and its mission to attract and inspire visitors is good for Cornwall, for horticulture, and for all the world's plants and crops. If Cornwall can show the way towards a more sustainable future, a greater love of plants and wildlife, daffodils will be there playing a part. Cornish horticultural entrepreneurs, be confident, you can do things that cannot be done elsewhere!

Daffodil Questions and Answers

Q. Why have my daffodils gone blind?

A. This is a frequent question, and is not easy to answer, simply because there can be several reasons why bulbs cease to flower. The most usual explanations are: mowing or trimming the leaves too early; the effect of increasing shade; competition from other plants; over-crowding of the bulbs; leaf disease, or a combination of these.

Q. Can I pick daffodil flowers without harming the bulbs?

A. Yes! Provided the leaves are not picked, but left full length and undamaged to continue to feed the bulb.

Q. Should I pick off the dead flowers?

A. Most definitely. 'Dead-heading' has two advantages for the bulbs. First, it saves the plant setting seed. Second, it removes a possible source of disease, since in damp weather *Botrytis* infects the dead flower, and the fungus which growers call 'fire' spreads to the leaves.

Q. If daffodils set seed, is this worth growing?

A. You may like to try it. The seed is best sown fairly fresh, about 2 cm deep, in late summer or autumn. It usually germinates the following spring. Unfortunately, it takes about five years for the plant to flower. Every daffodil raised from seed will be unique, even if the seeds come from the same pod. Your seedling daffodils will usually have nice flowers, but for real success you will need to start with some exceptional parents (daffodils that is!).

Q. Why are many of the most popular daffodil varieties so old?

A. It is estimated that from the time a breeder selects an outstanding plant from the seed-bed, it will take 20 years for it to increase to a tonne of bulbs. Even then it will take many more years before the grower can bring it on to the mass market. Daffodils with exceptional show quality are often sold much sooner, in smaller numbers, and at a high price.

Q. Who raises special show varieties?

A. These are produced by amateur or professional breeders, usually cross-pollinating the very latest varieties in their quest for excellence. Hybridizing old varieties seldom produces show-bench winners. However, rather few show varieties become large-scale commercial varieties because, though beautiful, they may not have a sufficiently robust constitution.

Q. When should daffodil bulbs be planted?
A. As early as possible. Growers mostly plant them before the end of August This results in stronger roots, earlier flowering and good bulb growth. Dried up, late-planted bulbs seldom do as well.

Q. If I have to wait to plant after the summer bedding, how should the bulbs be stored?
A. Store in a cool (17° C), well-ventilated place, either in shallow layers in trays, or in suspended nets. Some of the tazetta narcissi, such as 'Soleil d'Or', flower best when stored rather warm (25° C). Do not expose bulbs to bright sun – they can suffer sunburn!

Q. How can I avoid the need to keep digging up daffodil bulbs?
A. Planted in clusters with at least 15 cm (10 cm for miniatures) of soil over the bulbs, they can remain undisturbed for years. Mark their position with a stout label to avoid damaging the bulbs by future cultivation.

Q. What should I do with daffodil bulbs when I want to follow them with bedding plants?
A. It is not ideal to lift them in full growth, but they will withstand this provided the leaf is undamaged and they are replanted elsewhere promptly. Water thoroughly. The bulbs can be recovered later in the summer.

Q. How can I recover indoor potted bulbs so that they can be used in the garden?
A. After the flowers have faded, do not delay in planting them out. Remove the pot but do not break them apart. If left in the pot, dried out, starved or frosted, their chances of flowering the next year are poor.

Q. If daffodils can be left for years, why do commercial crops keep moving about?
A. Commercial crops stay in any one field for only two or three years. Rotation helps to keep them healthy, and the quality of the flowers is best on young, vigorous crops. Bulbs generally do not return to a previously used field for at least six years.

Q. Why are so many daffodil fields left unpicked?
A. In the first year after planting, the flowers may not be of the best size or quality for market, and so will often be left while the second and third year ones receive priority. Even fields which have been quite heavily picked will become yellow with unpicked, later flowers. Yet other reasons for wastage are a mild spell of weather, insufficient labour, and a glutted market. During the season, growers must maintain a continuity of supply to the market, so it is better to have a surplus rather than a gap.

Q. What are the best manures and fertilizers for daffodils?
A. Never use fresh manure before planting, and use compost sparingly. Daffodils are not heavy feeders; the greatest risk in rich ground is basal rot. Compost may, of course, be used as a mulch after planting. The main requirements are for a pH at or above 6.0, and sufficient phosphate and potash, especially the latter. Bone meal is often recommended, but it contains no potash, so if this is used, or 'Growmore' (analysis NPK 7:7:7), then additional sulphate of potash at 2oz per sq. yd. (67 g/m^2) is also needed. Mix fertilizers into the soil

before planting. 'Long-term' or naturalized bulbs benefit from an occasional top dressing of 'Growmore' in autumn.

Q. Why do some daffodil buds shrivel up without opening?
A. This is fairly common with double daffodils, especially the late-flowering ones. It generally means that the soil is dry and the site too warm.

Q. Which are the best kinds for scent?
A. All daffodils have some scent, but the strongest perfume is found in tazettas, jonquils and poets. With the exception of the more tender 'true' tazettas such as 'Soleil d'Or, 'Avalanche' and 'Primo', all kinds can be grown throughout Britain.

Q. What is the difference between a daffodil and a narcissus?
A. An old chestnut! Botanically, the whole genus is Narcissus, and all, as the RHS suggests, may be called daffodils. However, it is difficult to resist referring to the smaller and multi-headed ones as narcissi.

Q. How are bulbs sized? The packet may state 10–12 cm, or 12–14 cm.
A. Sizes are quoted in centimetres circumference, not diameter!

Some Dos and Don'ts of Daffodil Growing

- Do try to plant daffodil bulbs early, preferably no later than September.

- Do not dry bulbs in direct sunshine.

- Do not allow pots, tubs or planters to freeze in winter, or the bulbs will be killed.

- Do not delay in planting out potted bulbs after they have finished flowering.

- Do not mow off naturalized daffodils until there are signs of the leaves yellowing.

- Do plant daffodils for naturalizing in a place where you do not mind delaying mowing.

- Do not cut or tie up daffodil leaves while they are still green.

- Do be very careful with weed killers, which can be translocated downwards and kill the bulbs. After planting bulbs in pots or pans, place sand or gravel over the top of them to prevent the new roots forcing the bulb up. Most bulbs then need a period in a cool, damp place to grow good roots.

- Before forcing bulbs in warmth, ensure that they are well rooted, and the tip of the flower bud is just visible between the leaves.

- Do not try to grow bulbs in waterlogged ground.

- Do not use fresh manure for bulbs.

- Do ensure that daffodils have sufficient potash in the soil, and give them a feed of 'Growmore' each autumn.

- Avoid planting in shade. Without sunshine, the bulbs will decline and flowering cease.

- Do dig up and destroy any unhealthy plants. Virus, basal rot and eelworm can spread to neighbouring plants.

Appendices

Appendix 1: Some of the principal present-day commercial daffodil varieties grown in Cornwall

The varieties are listed in their approximate order of flowering in Cornwall, from the earliest, 'Rijnveld's Early Sensation' in December/January to 'Ultimus' in late April. The flowering of many early varieties has become earlier since the mid-1960s, while most late ones remain late.

Variety	Division and colour	Date of registration or (date of first recorded flowering)	Origin
Rijnveld's Early Sensation	1Y-Y	1956	England
Jedna	1Y-Y	1985	Cornwall
Barenwyn	1Y-Y	1985	Cornwall
Tamara	2Y-Y	1980	Cornwall
Mando	1Y-Y	1959	Northern Ireland
Dutch Master	1Y-Y	(pre 1938)	Holland
Hollywood	2Y-O	(pre 1939)	Holland
Golden Harvest	1Y-Y	(pre 1920)	Holland
Emblyn	2Y-Y	1989	Cornwall
California	2Y-Y	(pre 1927)	Cornwall
Malvern City	1Y-Y	(pre 1951)	New Zealand
Crewenna	2W-Y	1985	Cornwall
Loveday	2Y-O	1985	Cornwall
Trousseau	1W-Y	(pre 1934)	Cornwall
Dellan	2Y-Y	1989	Cornwall
St Keverne	2Y-Y	(1934)	Cornwall
Ice Follies	2W-W	(pre 1934)	Holland
Carlton	2Y-Y	(pre 1927)	Cornwall
Martinette	7Y-O	1985	USA/Cornwall
Golden Ducat	4Y-Y	(pre 1947)	Holland
Standard Value	1Y-Y	(pre 1949)	Holland
White Lion	4W-WYY	(pre 1949)	Holland
Counsellor	1Y-Y	(pre 1935)	Northern Ireland
Cheerfulness	4W-Y	(pre1923)	Holland
Yellow Cheerfulness	4Y-Y	(pre 1937)	Holland
Lothario	2W-Y	(pre 1938)	Holland
Ultimus	2Y-O	(pre 1947)	Holland

Appendix 2: Some of the principal present-day narcissi grown on the Isles of Scilly

The varieties are listed in approximate order of flowering, from 'Paper White' in October/November to 'Golden Dawn' in March.

In former times the Isles produced much the same varieties as the Cornish mainland, but always grew many of the rather tender tazetta narcissi (Division 8). As competition and acreage on the mainland increased, Island growers have specialized in these scented, winter-flowering tazettas.

Some cultural techniques are used to advance or retard the flowering of tazetta narcissi. This is indicated for 'Grand Soleil d'Or', the main variety grown, which therefore appears three times in the following list.

Variety	Division andcolour	Date of registration or (date of first recorded flowering)	Origin
Paper White	8W-W	(pre 1887)	Mediterranean
Innisidgen	8Y-O	1982	Cornwall
White Pearl	8W-W	(pre 1861)	Uncertain
Grand Soleil d'Or (Advanced)	8Y-O	(pre 1770)	Mediterranean
Hugh Town	8Y-O	1987	USA/Cornwall
Grand Primo	8W-Y	(pre 1780)	Mediterranean
Grand Soleil d'Or (Natural)	8Y-O	(pre 1770)	Mediterranean
Erlicheer	4W-Y	(pre 1934)	Australia
Avalanche	8W-Y	(pre 1906)	Cornwall
Scilly Valentine	8Y-O	1995	USA/Cornwall
Royal Connection	8Y-O	1995	USA/Cornwall
Grand Soleil d'Or (Retarded)	8Y-O	(pre 1770)	Mediterranean
Cheerfulness	4W-Y	(pre 1923)	Holland
Sir Winston Churchill	4W-O	1966	Unknown
Grand Monarque	8W-Y	(pre 1798)	Uncertain
Silver Chimes	8W-W	(pre 1914)	Cornwall
Golden Dawn	8Y-O	1958	USA

Appendix 3: Some of the principal commercial daffodil varieties grown in Cornwall in the second half of the twentieth century

Some of these varieties are still grown today, while others have passed into obscurity.

The flowering of many early varieties has become much earlier in recent years, while late varieties tend to remain late.

The varieties are listed in their approximate order of flowering in Cornwall, from 'Magnificence' in February to *Narcissus poeticus flore pleno* (Double White) in mid-May.

Variety	Division and colour	Date of registration or (date of first recorded flowering)	Origin
Magnificence	1Y-Y	(pre 1914)	England
Golden Harvest	1Y-Y	(pre 1920)	Holland
Hollywood	2Y-O	(pre 1939)	Holland
California	2Y-Y	(pre 1927)	Cornwall
Helios	2Y-O	(pre 1912)	England
Finland	2W-Y	(pre 1940)	Cornwall
Brunswick	2W-Y	(pre 1931)	Cornwall
Flower Carpet	1Y-Y	(pre 1948)	Unknown
Rembrandt	1Y-Y	(pre 1926)	Holland
Fortune	2Y-O	(pre 1917)	England
King Alfred	1Y-Y	(pre 1899)	England
Armada	2Y-O	(pre 1938)	Northern Ireland
Unsurpassable	1Y-Y	(pre 1923)	Holland
Carlton	2Y-Y	(pre 1927)	Cornwall
Edward Buxton	3Y-YYO	(pre 1932)	England
Aflame	3W-YOO	(pre 1938)	Holland
Red Devon	2Y-O	(pre 1943	England
Burgemeester Gouverneur	1Y-Y	(pre 1930)	Holland
Mount Hood	1W-W	(pre 1938)	Holland
St Agnes	8W-O	(pre 1926)	Cornwall
Flower Record	2W-YYO	(pre 1934)	Holland
Aranjuez	2Y-YYO	(pre 1932)	Holland

Variety	Division and colour	Date of registration or (date of first recorded flowering)	Origin
Inglescombe	4Y-Y	(pre 1912)	England
White Lion	4W-WYY	(pre 1949)	Holland
Winifred van Graven	3W-YYR	(pre 1954)	Holland
Actaea	9W-YYR	(pre 1927)	Holland
Verger	3W-R	(pre 1930)	Holland
Geranium	8W-O	(pre 1930)	Holland
Cheerfulness	4W-Y	(pre 1923)	Holland
Kilworth	2W-YOO	(pre 1938)	Ireland
White Sail	4W-W	(pre 1946)	Holland
Narcissus poeticus recurvus	13W-GYR	Species	Alpine Europe
Narcissus poeticus flore pleno	4W-W	Species (double)	Uncertain

Appendix 4: Some of the principal varieties of daffodils grown commercially in Cornwall in the first half of the twentieth century

Very few of these varieties are seen today, other than in specialist catalogues or as semi-wild escapes from cultivation. The varieties are listed in their approximate order of flowering in Cornwall, from 'The First' to *Narcissus poeticus flore pleno* (Double White).

Variety	Division and colour	Date of first recorded flowering	Origin
The First	1Y-Y	1921	Holland
Narcissus obvallaris (The Tenby daffodil)	13Y-Y	pre 1873	Uncertain
Sulphur	1Y-Y	pre 1927	Cornwall
Van Sion (Telamonius Plenus)	4Y-Y	pre 1620	Uncertain
Maximus Superbus	1Y-Y	pre 1851	Uncertain
Golden Spur	1Y-Y	pre 1885	Holland
Helios	2Y-O	pre 1912	England
Hospodar	2Y-O	pre 1914	Cornwall
King Alfred	1Y-Y	pre 1899	England
Princeps	1W-Y	pre 1830	Uncertain
Henry Irving	1Y-Y	pre 1885	Holland
Sir Watkin	2Y-Y	pre 1868	Uncertain
Havelock	2Y-Y	pre 1927	Cornwall
W.P. Milner	1W-W	pre 1869	England
Coverack Glory	2Y-Y	pre 1927	Cornwall
Corinthian	1Y-Y	pre 1931	Cornwall
Bath's Flame	3Y-YYO	pre 1913	England
Lucifer	2W-YOO	pre 1890	Ireland
Empress	1W-Y	pre 1869	England
Lady Margaret Boscawen	2W-Y	pre 1887	Holland
Scarlet Gem	8Y-O	pre 1910	Cornwall
Bernardino	2W-Y	pre 1907	England
Croesus	2Y-YYO	pre 1912	Cornwall
Emperor	1Y-Y	pre 1869	England
Horsfieldii	1W-Y	c. 1845	England
Barrii Conspicuus	3Y-YYO	pre 1869	England
Horace	9W-GOR	pre 1894	England
Hexameter	9W-GYR	c. 1923	England
Narcissus poeticus recurvus	13W-GYR	Species	Alpine Europe
Narcissus poeticus flore pleno	4W-W	Species (double)	Uncertain

Appendix 5: A selection of dwarf or semi-dwarf varieties of daffodils for small gardens or container growing

The varieties are listed in approximate order of flowering, from the earliest, 'February Gold' to the latest to flower, 'Sun Disc'.

Variety	Division and colour	Date of registration or (date of first recorded flowering)	Origin
February Gold	6Y-Y	(pre 1923)	Holland
Narcissus obvallaris (The Tenby Daffodil)	13Y-Y	(pre 1873)	Uncertain
Tête à Tête	12 Y-Y	1949	Cornwall
Jumblie	12 Y-O	(pre 1952)	Cornwall
Quince	12 Y-Y	(pre 1953)	Cornwall
Jack Snipe	6W-Y	(pre 1951)	Cornwall
Jenny	6W-W	(pre 1943)	England
Dove Wings	6W-Y	(pre 1949)	England
Eaton Song	12 Y-O	1989	USA/Cornwall
Cornish Chuckles	12 Y-Y	1996	USA/Cornwall
Jetfire	6Y-O	1966	USA
March Sunshine	6Y-Y	(pre 1923)	Holland
Ice Wings	5W-W	1958	England
Charity May	6Y-Y	(pre 1948)	England
Minnow	8Y-Y	1962	Cornwall
Pipit	7YYW-W	1963	USA
Segovia	3W-Y	1962	Cornwall
Sundial	7Y-Y	1955	Cornwall
Sun Disc	7Y-Y	1946	Cornwall

Appendix 6: A selection of medium to tall varieties of daffodils, representing all divisions 1-9, suitable for the garden

These daffodils have been selected to flower in succession over the whole season, from 'Rijn-veld's Early Sensation' to 'After All' and *Narcissus poeticus recurvus*, which are the latest to bloom. The list seeks to exclude varieties with brittle stems or heavy heads. Most of the following have received an RHS Award of Garden Merit. (A succession of yellow daffodils providing a long season of flowering might include: 'Rijnveld's Early Sensation', 'January Gold', 'February Gold', 'St Keverne', 'Carlton', 'Irish Luck' and 'Counsellor'.)

Variety (Year of RHS Award of Garden Merit)	Division and colour	Date of registration or (date of first recorded flowering)	Origin
Rijnveld's Early Sensation (1993)	1Y-Y	1956 (1943)	England
January Gold	6Y-Y	1985	Cornwall – registered as 'First Hope'
Dutch Master (1995)	1Y-Y	(pre 1938)	Holland
St Keverne (1993)	2Y-Y	(1934)	Cornwall
Trousseau	1W-Y	(pre 1934)	Cornwall
Barrett Browning	3WWY-O	(1945)	Holland
Ice Follies (1993)	2W-W	(pre 1953)	Holland
Carlton (1995)	2Y-Y	(pre 1927)	Cornwall
Red Devon (1993)	2Y-O	(pre 1943)	England
Tibet (1964)	2W-W	(pre 1942)	Northern Ireland
Cragford	8W-O	(pre 1930)	Cornwall
Sweetness (1973)	7Y-Y	(pre 1938)	Cornwall
St Patrick's Day	2Y-Y	1964	Holland
Mount Hood (1995)	1W-W	(pre 1938)	Holland
Irish Luck	1Y-Y	(pre 1948)	Northern Ireland
Tamar Fire	4Y-R	1976	Ireland
Thalia	5W-W	(pre 1914)	Holland
Suzy (1993)	7Y-O	(pre 1954)	Cornwall
Tresamble (1958)	5W-W	(pre 1930)	Cornwall
Salome (1971)	2W-PPY	1958	Ireland
Actaea (1993)	9W-YYR	(pre 1927)	Holland
Geranium (1995)	8W-O	(pre 1930)	Holland
Counsellor	1Y-Y	(pre 1935)	Northern Ireland
Cheerfulness (1995)	4W-Y	(pre 1923)	Holland
Yellow Cheerfulness (1995)	4Y-Y	(pre 1937)	Holland
Lothario	2W-Y	(pre 1938)	Holland
After All	3W-YYR	1961	Holland
Narcissus poeticus recurvus	13-GYR	Species	Alpine Europe

Appendix 7: Daffodil classification over the years

The RHS *Dictionary of Gardening* states that there are some 50 species of narcissi. The actual figure was, for many years, a matter for keen debate by daffodil enthusiasts. Some early botanists, known as 'splitters', named huge numbers of species on the basis of small differences in the character of the flower or plant, while others, the 'lumpers', considered this excessively fussy, preferring to create simple groupings. In 1762, Linnaeus, the famous plant classifier, pronounced that there were 13 species of narcisssi and, according to A.E. Bowles, would have considered some classifiers as 'either rabid florists or over-meticulous observers of minute details'. In 1831, one such person, A.H. Haworth, described 16 different genera containing no less than 148 species. Later, other 'splitters' observing different forms of the flower increased the 'species' count to about 400.

In his 1888 *Handbook of Amaryllideae*, J.G. Baker proposed a single genus of 16 species, 11 hybrids, 26 subspecies and 13 with Latin names – a total of 66, which is broadly accepted today.

The classification of daffodils has undergone many changes over the years. The RHS has played a central role, and in 1908 produced the first classified list. At about that time, three main groups – the Magni, Medii and Parvicoronati (quaintly known as the 'Coffee-cup', 'Tea-cup' and 'Tea-saucer' sections, according to the length of the corona or cup) – held sway. Within these groups there existed a string of wonderful and imaginative sub-groups, such as 'Incomparabilis', or families bearing the name of a particular breeder or enthusiast. Thus 'Leedsii', after Edward Leeds (1802–77), and 'Barrii', after Peter Barr (1826–1909), were widely used names, much as we speak of 'Williamsii' camellias today.

Clearly, the system was getting out of hand. The 11 divisions created in the 1908 list brought a welcome breath of fresh air at a time when the crossing and inter-crossing of the major groups was resulting in confusion due to an enormous increase in the number of hybrids. Today, after quite a lot of tidying up, there are 12 reasonably clear divisions, plus one more for those that do not seem to fit in elsewhere.

The classification of daffodils

1998 Revised classification	1908 Classification	Pre 1908 Classification
Division 1 Trumpet	I Trumpet	Magnicoronati
Division 2 Large-cupped	II Incomparabilis	Mediicoronati
Division 3 Small-cupped	III Barrii	Mediicoronati
Division 4 Double	IV Leedsii	Mediicoronati
Division 5 Triandrus	V Triandrus	
Division 6 Cyclamineus	VI Cyclamineus	
Division 7 Jonquilla	VII Jonquilla	
Division 8 Tazetta	VIII Tazetta	Parvicoronati
Division 9 Poeticus	IX Poeticus	Parvicoronati
Division 10 Bulbocodium	X Double	
Division 11 Split corona	XI Species and hybrids	
Division 12 Others		
Division 13 Botanical		

Glossary of Terms Used in Daffodil Growing

basal rot: a troublesome fungus disease which rots the bulb. It is caused by *Fusarium*.

bud abortion: sometimes known as 'blasting', in which the bud dies. If conditions are unsuitable, this can take place at any stage from initiation to just before flowering.

bulb grading: a term loosely covering several operations. Bulbs passing over a grading machine are cleaned, inspected, sorted and sized.

bulb size (cm): bulbs are sized by centimetres circumference, by passing them over a succession of gradually widening riddles.

bulb types: mother bulb – a large bulb consisting of several units or 'noses'; double-nosed bulb – a premium bulb with two 'noses'; round bulb – a single unit with no side, or offset bulbs; offset or chip – side bulbs usually separated from a main bulb in order to increase the stock.

burning-over: a traditional practice in the Isles of Scilly, which advances and improves the growth of narcissi of the Tazetta group (Division 8).

chipping: a propagation technique which is simpler than twin-scaling and can be mechanized.

classification: a system of grouping plants (narcissi) according to parentage and characteristics.

clone: a genetically uniform stock of bulbs (or any plant) derived originally from a single individual, propagated only by vegetative means.

cold requirement: the amount of cold treatment (or cold weather) required before a bulb will grow normally. Sometimes expressed as weeks at 9° C (48° F).

contact herbicide: kills by contact only.

cool chain: holding the product in cold storage throughout its passage from grower to customer.

de-stoning: a pre-planting operation to remove stones from the zone of soil where the bulbs are to be planted. It facilitates future harvesting of the bulbs.

direct harvesting: harvested bulbs taken in bulk directly indoors for artificial drying.

divisions 1–13: the RHS system of classifying daffodils according to their flower type and botanical origins.

emasculation: the removal of pollen-bearing parts of the flower in breeding new varieties. Prevents self-pollination of the flower.

flower initiation: the formation of a microscopic flower at the growing point of the bulb in the summer before flowering.

forcing: advancing growth and flowering by placing in warmth (e.g., heated glasshouse). Bulbs for forcing are often specially treated (prepared) by applying cold storage, without which they will often fail to grow properly.

goose-neck stage: a stage of picking or marketing where the bud has bent over. The bud sheath may have split, but the flower is not open.

ground keepers: bulbs left behind after harvesting. Unless killed or dug out the next spring, these persist and 'bridge' (nullify) the rotation.

hot-water treatment (HWT): soaking bulbs in hot (warm) water primarily to kill pests within the bulb.

lily rash: skin irritation caused by daffodil juice (or pollen), and attributed to crystals of oxalic acid.

micropropagation (= tissue culture): division and culturing of small pieces of plant material under sterile conditions in a laboratory.

mutant or mutation: see **sport**.

pc stage: the completion of flower initiation with the formation of the miniature trumpet or cup (paracorolla) of the daffodil.

pencil stage: an early stage of picking or marketing, while the bud is upright and un-opened.

potato cyst nematode (PCN): a serious pest of potatoes whose presence in the land can restrict the sale of bulbs upon which the nematode can be carried. Regulations are particularly strict for exports to the USA.

pre-cooling: a lengthy period of cool storage applied to bulbs before planting, to advance subsequent growth and flowering.

pre-soaking: a cold-water soak used immediately before hot-water treatment, specifically intended to improve the kill of bulb eelworm. It particularly follows the pre-warming treatment.

pre-warming: a period of warm storage applied immediately before hot-water treatment, which minimized any adverse effects of the treatment on subsequent growth and flowering.

residual herbicide: herbicide that persists in the soil, killing mainly seedling weeds.

rogue: a bulb of the wrong variety appearing in a stock.

roguing: the removal of a 'rogue' bulb by inspection and digging out.

rotation: a sequence of different crops that reduces the build-up of pests and diseases. Daffodils do not normally return to the same field for six years or more.

senescence: the death of the foliage. Premature senescence may be caused by disease or other adverse factors.

smoking: a development from the burning-over technique in which the active agent – smoke – is used to advance growth.

soil sickness: a complex of pests and diseases caused by a lack of rotation. The pathogens cause root rot.

spickels: small, yellowish, raised bumps on leaves – the first symptom of eelworm.

sport (synonym: mutant or mutation): a spontaneous variant appearing in a stock. An example would be the appearance of 'Golden Ducat', a double sport of the trumpet daffodil, 'King Alfred'.

stem and bulb eelworm: one of the most serious pests of daffodils. Eelworms are also known as nematodes.

tissue culture: see **micropropagation**.

translocated herbicide: absorbed by the plant, and moved within it to kill the roots of perennial weeds.

twin-scaling: a propagation technique.

virgin land: land which has not grown daffodils before. This is the best land.

virus-free stock: bulbs which have been rendered free form virus infection by advanced laboratory techniques.

windrowing: bulbs lifted and left for a while to dry on the surface of the ground.

Bibliography and Further Reading

Baker, J.G. (1888), *Handbook of Amaryllideae*. London: George Bell & Sons.

Barr, P. (1884), *A Lyttle Boke of Ye Narcissus or Daffodyl Flowre and hys Roots*. London: King Strete, Westminster.

Barnes, D. (1989), *Daffodils*. Newton Abbot: David & Charles.

Blanchard, J.W. (1990), *Narcissus*. Woking: Alpine Garden Society.

Bourne, S.E. (1914), *The Book of the Daffodil*. London: John Lane.

Bowles, A.E. (1934), *The Narcissus*. London: Waterstone.

Bowley, R.L. (1945), *The Fortunate Islands*. St Mary's, Isles of Scilly: Bowley Publications.

Bryan, J.E. (1989), *Bulbs*. 2 vols. London: Christopher Helm.

Burbidge, F.W. (1875), *The Narcissus: Its History and Culture*. London: L Reeve.

Calvert, A.F. (1929), *Daffodil Growing for Pleasure and Profit*. London: Dulau.

Carson, R. (1963), *Silent Spring*. London: Hamish Hamilton.

De Hertogh, A. & Le Nard, M. (1993), *The Physiology of Flower Bulbs*. London: Elsevier.

Dobbs, R.C. (1983), *Bulbs in Britain: A Century of Growing*. Spalding: self-published.

Gray, A. (1955), *Miniature Daffodils*. London: Collingridge.

Grey-Wilson, C., Mathew, B., & Blamey, M. (1981), *Bulbs*. London: Collins.

Hanks, G.R. (ed.) (2002), *Narcissus and Daffodil*. London: Taylor & Francis.

Heath, B.C. (1995), *Daffodils for American Gardens*. Washington, USA: Elliott & Clark.

Jefferson-Brown, M. (1991), *Narcissus*. London: Batsford.

MAFF/HMSO publications:

Bulb and Corm Production. Ref. Book 62, 1984 (5th edn.)

Diseases of Bulbs. Ref. Book HPD 1, 1979 (2nd edn.)

Bulb Pests. Ref. Book 51, 1984 (7th edn.)

Hot-water treatment of plant material. Formerly *Bulletin 201, 1986* (3rd edn.)

Mathew, B. (1986), *The Year Round Bulb Garden*. London: Souvenir Press.

— (1987), *The Smaller Bulbs*. London: Batsford.

Mock, R. (2001), *A Cornish Rhapsody: From a Penny-halfpenny an Hour to a Fortune*. Penzance: Mount's Bay Press.

Mumford, C. (1967), *Portrait of the Isles of Scilly*. London: Robert Hale.

Page, W. (ed.) (1906), *Victoria History of Cornwall*. London: James Street.

Rix, M. & Phillips, R. (1981), *The Bulb Book*. London: Pan.

Rix, M. (1983), *Growing Bulbs*. London: Croom Helm.

Royal Horticultural Society (1992), *RHS Dictionary of Gardening*. London: Macmillan.

—, *The Daffodil Yearbook*, 1942. London: RHS.

—, *The Daffodil and Tulip Yearbook*, 1946 to 1971. London: RHS.

—, *Daffodils*, 1972 to 1992–3. London: RHS.

—, *Daffodils and Tulips*, 1994–5 to 2001–2. London: RHS.

—, *Daffodils with Snowdrops and Tulips*, 2002–3 to 2004–5. London: RHS.

—, *The International Daffodil Register and Classified List, 1998 plus supplements*. London: RHS.

Skelmersdale, C. (1989), *Bulbs*. London: W.I. Books.

Smit, T. (1997), *The Lost Gardens of Heligan*. London: Gollancz.

Wells, J.S. (1989), *Modern Miniature Daffodils*. London: Batsford.

Index

Note: Daffodil varieties are listed first under each letter of the alphabet.

Acknowledgements

Photographs are reproduced by kind permission of: The Ellbridge Archive, pages 92 (bottom), 109; Gibsons of Scilly, pages 18, 19, 27, 100, 101; Martin Goodey, pages 77 (right), 83 (bottom), 84; Peter Hobson, pages 113, 125; Horticultural Research International, page 72; MAFF, pages 57, 59 (top left and right), 60 (top left and right); Ron Scamp, pages 50 (left), 83 (top), 107; Andrew Tompsett, pages 12 (top), 13–17, 20–21, 22, 30, 36, 37 (top), 38, 46, 47, 51, 52, 55, 56 (top right, bottom), 60 (mid right, bottom right), 61, 62, 66, 67 (top, bottom left and right), 70 (bottom), 73, 75, 76, 78, 82, 85–7, 88 (left), 89, 91, 96, 97, 102 (top), 103 (bottom), 104 (top), 105, 106, 110, 111, 114 (top), 116 (top), 117 (top left), 122, 141; Western Morning News, page 108 (top). The source of the photograph on page 49 is unknown.

The picture of P.D. Williams on page 54 is from *Daffodils*, 1986–7; the photograph of James Ramsbottom on page 70 is from *The Daffodil Yearbook*, 1940, and that of Alec Gray on page 56 is from *The Daffodil and Tulip Yearbook*, 1961. The drawings of daffodils on pages 63–5 are taken from *The International Daffodil Register*, 1998. All of these are reproduced by permission of the Royal Horticultural Society. The *Daffodil Yearbooks* are no longer in print, but the Yearbook is still published annually as *Daffodils with Snowdrops and Tulips*, available from the Royal Horticultural Society: www.rhs.org.uk. All other photographs were taken by Peter Phelan in 2002–03.

The author and Peter Phelan wish to thank the many growers who gave them generous help, and access to their farms.

The author gratefully acknowledges the assistance of Dr Lesley Atkinson in editing his manuscript, and Dr A. Bromley for slide scans. The financial support of the Stanley Smith (UK) Horticultural Trust and the Sir Arthur Quiller Couch Memorial Fund is also gratefully recorded. Finally, the author also thanks his wife, Pamela, for scanning, checking and encouraging.

Note: The 1964 photograph of the Sou'westers Horticultural Club on page 49 shows, from left to right, standing: N. Treseder, E.C. Penna, G.H. Simmons, H.J. Eaton (Station Director), E.P. Lello, M.S. Banfield, R. Tomlin; seated: A.E. Gunningham, A.C. Tomlin, F.B. Secrett, Miss K.H. Johnstone, K.C. Tewkesbury, J.W. Godber, C. Le Grice, H.W. Abbisss.